Delicious meals
made simple

for people managing symptoms

Astrid Slettenaar

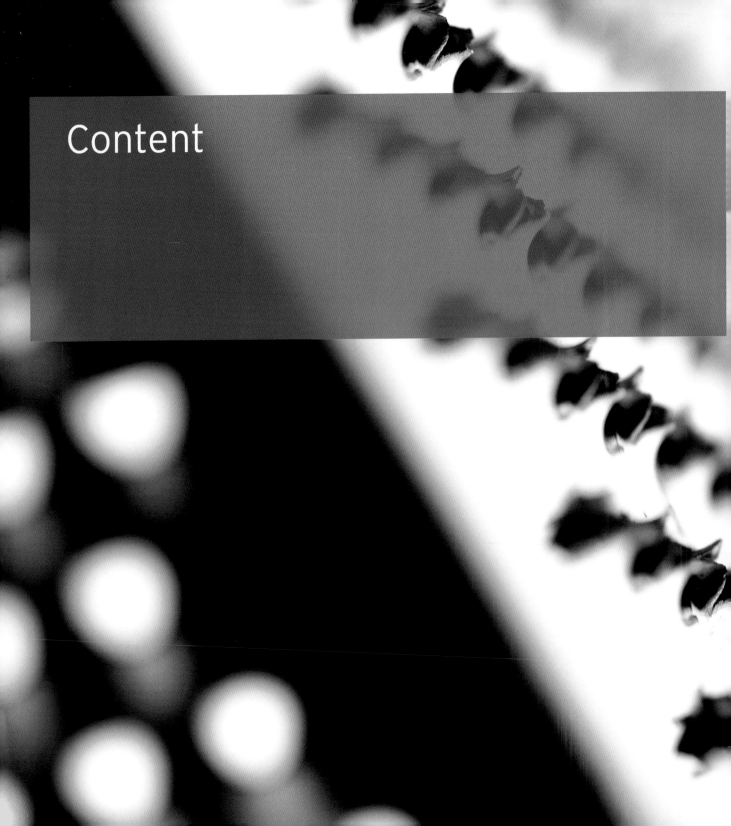

Content

Foreword

Bread on the table: as straightforward as that may have been centuries before, it is no longer the case in our contemporary western society. There are dozens of different types of bread to choose from at the baker or supermarket, and a lot of people are easily swayed by a scrumptious roll or special delicacy. This applies to all our food: regardless of how simple the meal is, we consciously opt for the palatable and the healthy, which, if possible, is prudent for both ourselves and the environment.

Numerous cookbooks catering to contemporary needs have invariably been introduced into the market. Delicious recipes suitable for any moment of the day, ranging from cheap to expensive, simple to elaborate or from a casserole to a seven-course meal for eight people.

This cookbook belongs in none of those categories. Naturally, it contains tasty recipes, that's a given. But it's written from a completely different perspective - one that is so often overlooked - that these delicious recipes still need to be prepared. And when you have lost the sensation in your fingers or need to conserve your body's energy or have limited mobility, then serving up a healthy, well-balanced meal every day can be a bit of a challenge.

At this juncture, I'm proud to say that my sister came up with the idea to solve this oversight. She is a practical woman. A doer, a go-getter with unlimited determination. While growing up as the youngest of the local kids and who couldn't yet ride a bike, although the rest could, she found a way with which she could still participate in their fun. She taught herself to run very fast, which enabled her to keep up with them as they rode their bikes. It's not surprising that of all people it was my sister, Astrid, who developed the idea for the book lying in front of you. She started out as a nurse in the department of neurology at one of the largest non-academic hospitals in the Netherlands, the Medical Spectrum Twente, and eventually specialised in the field of MS. After qualifying as an MS specialist nurse, she went on to independently establish an MS Outpatient Clinic in Enschede and oversee the introduction of the same health care facility in other hospitals. Last year she received her Nurse Practitioner's Diploma

and is currently working as a Clinical Nurse Specialist. Of course, she continued to delve into functional applications: within the caucus of national and even international consultative bodies associated with MS and by recently organising the first national MS-Youth Day, as an example.

And now, there is this cookbook. You could say that this book is a culmination of her endeavours and everything that Astrid has paid particular attention to over the years. It is a product of her acquired experience, vast knowledge and the many contacts throughout the world of MS. A book full of recipes that practically and concretely integrates into everyday life. Because people with MS - which can exhibit varying symptoms - come across problems, big and small, every day. That's why the recipes correspond to a variety of symptoms and situations, punctuated here and there with useful tips.

I'm guessing that a lot of people will be glad with this cookbook. Even people who don't suffer from MS, but are nevertheless restricted in their abilities.

For my part, I chose to work in Mental Healthcare. And as testimony to its appropriateness, I will say that I often discern in conversation the need for practical and concrete help, which is exactly what this cookbook provides. I am convinced that with this cookbook, my sister has made a valuable contribution to the daily lives of people suffering from MS.

I imagine this book is only the start of a series of new and practical ideas that will help make life easier. Keep up the good work, sis!

Kirsten Slettenaar

Introduction

When you've been diagnosed with multiple sclerosis (MS), you're still allowed to eat and drink whatever you like. A special regimen isn't provided by the attending health professionals, such as the neurologist and MS specialist nurse, but a healthy and varied diet is recommended. Symptoms often arise from MS that generally affect your eating habits and hinder the manner in which you prepare food.

The recipes in this cookbook correspond to various symptoms commonly associated with MS. For example there are quick recipes that take fatigue into consideration. For others, preparation times are longer so it's important to take the necessary time. And sensory disturbances of the hands require an adjustment in cooking methods. Furthermore, this book contains some light, refreshing recipes that could help alleviate your symptoms in the hot summer months.

I'm proud of the fact that the first cookbook, compiled for people suffering from MS, is in your possession. In addition to various quick and easy recipes, this book also gives practical advice on how to plan meals and utilise necessary items. This book is largely divided into chapters associated with symptoms, making it easier to find dishes suited to your particular situation.

Weights and measures
100 g(rams) = 3.5 oz
100 ml = 3.5 fl. oz
1 litre = 35 fl. oz
1 dl = 3.5 fl. oz

Fact   Important when coping with multiple sclerosis (or not!): relax and have fun. Don't let stress and strain get the upper hand. Even during cooking. Taking pleasure in what you do ensures a more engaged and better focused you.

Tip   So before you start cooking poor youself a drink and relax. Here you go...

1. Cooking and fatigue

Eighty percent of people diagnosed with MS suffer from fatigue. This is often a chronic tiredness not directly associated with exertion. Certainly after a tiring day with your family or being at work, the question is whether or not you have any energy left to prepare a healthy meal. These recipes can also be used during a relapse when fatigue often increases.

This chapter includes recipes containing all the essential nutrients you need, but are still quick to prepare.

Servings are for four persons.

Spicy chicken salad

Preparation time: 5 minutes

2 tablespoons olive oil
400 g chicken fillet, diced
350 g pre-cooked, diced potatoes
4 tablespoons red curry paste
salt
1 small courgette
200 g mixed lettuce
1 bottle of herb salad dressing

1 Heat the oil in a pan and fry the chicken, potatoes and curry paste for 5 minutes. Add salt to taste.

2 Cut the courgette in half lengthwise and remove the seeds with a teaspoon. Cut the courgette into thin slices, put in a bowl and mix together with the lettuce.

3 Arrange the salad onto the plates and place the chicken and potatoes on top. Serve the dressing on the side.

Serving suggestion: with pappadums.

Tip You often have more energy in the mornings than you do at the end of the afternoon. Therefore, you could choose to cook during the lunch hours and have your warm meal then. In the evening all you need to do is prepare a sandwich, thus conserving your energy.

Braised pork in sweet soy sauce

Preparation time: 5 minutes

300 g diced pork
125 g bacon strips
3 tablespoons lemon juice
2 tablespoons sunflower oil
400 g Thai stir-fry vegetables with red pepper
5 tablespoons Indonesian sweet soy sauce
100 ml hot water
salt and (freshly ground) pepper

1 Mix the diced pork in a bowl together with the strips of bacon and lemon juice.

2 Heat the oil in a frying pan. Stir-fry the meat and vegetables over high heat for 2 minutes.

3 Add the soy sauce and 100 ml of hot water and allow the contents to stew for 3 minutes. Add salt and pepper to taste.

Serving suggestion: with white rice and prawn crackers.

Stir-fried broccoli with baby corn and cashew nuts

Preparation time: 10 minutes

4 tablespoons (stir-fry) oil
1 red onion, in rings
2 cloves of garlic, sliced
100 g baby corn
150 g mushrooms, sliced
400 g broccoli florets
2 tablespoons ginger syrup
2 tablespoons lime juice
salt and (freshly ground) pepper
100 g cashew nuts

1 Heat the oil in a wok and sauté the onion and garlic. Add the baby corn, mushrooms and broccoli and stir-fry over high heat for 3-4 minutes.

2 Add 3 tablespoons of water, the ginger syrup and the lime juice and heat the vegetables for another 2-3 minutes.

3 Add salt and pepper to taste and spoon in the nuts.

Serving suggestion: with Chinese noodles or rice.

Spicy omelette with onions and tomatoes

Preparation time: 10 minutes

2 tablespoons olive oil
2 onions, finely chopped
salt and (freshly ground) pepper
1 pack of cherry tomatoes
1 spring onion, cut into rings
8 eggs
4 tablespoons finely cut fresh herbs (oregano, parsley, basil)
30 g butter
1 tub cucumber salad

1 Heat the oil in a pan and sauté the onion. Add salt and pepper to taste. Cover the pot with a lid and allow the onions to braise for 5 minutes. Cut the tomatoes in half and add these to the onions together with the spring onion for the final 2 minutes.

2 Beat the eggs lightly in a bowl. Stir in the onions, tomatoes and 3 tablespoons of herbs and add a little more salt and pepper to taste.

3 Melt half the quantity of butter in a non-stick pan and pour half of the egg mixture in. Cook the omelette on a low heat until the underside is golden brown and the top is nearly set. Flip the omelette with a spatula and cook the other side until it too turns golden brown. Prepare the second omelette in the same way.

4 Cut the omelettes into 8 pieces and arrange these onto a flat dish or plate. Sprinkle the pieces with the remaining herbs.

5 Serve with a helping of cucumber salad.

Serving suggestion: with (white) bread.

Mexican wrap with cod and shrimps

Preparation time: 10 minutes

400 g cod (frozen), diced
1 teaspoon taco seasoning
salt and (freshly ground) pepper
3 tablespoons sunflower oil
1 jar hot salsa
125 g shrimps, cooked and peeled
4 wrap tortillas
125 ml sour cream
200 g shredded iceberg lettuce

1 Flavour the cod well with the taco seasoning, salt and pepper.

2 Heat the oil in a non-stick pan. Cook the diced fish on one side until golden brown. Turn the fish carefully over with a fish slice or spatula and cook the other side.

3 Add the salsa sauce and the shrimp and heat the contents of the pan for 2 minutes. Add salt and pepper to taste.

4 Fry the tortillas on both sides in a pan until crisp. Coat the tortillas with sour cream, layer with lettuce and spoon the fish mixture on top. Fold the tortillas in half.

5 Serve with the rest of the lettuce.

Serving suggestion: with guacamole and cherry tomatoes.

Spaghetti with quick Bolognese sauce

Preparation time: 15 minutes

300 g whole-wheat spaghetti
salt
2 tablespoons olive oil
2 onions, finely chopped
2 cloves of garlic, finely chopped
300 g minced beef
1 carton sieved tomatoes (500 g)
1 tin diced tomatoes (400 g)
1 beef stock cube
1 teaspoon dried or 1 tablespoon fresh Italian
    seasoning

cayenne pepper
75 g Parmesan cheese, coarsely grated

1 Cook the pasta according to the package directions in salt water until al dente, then allow the pasta to drain in a colander.

2 Heat the oil in a frying pan and fry the chopped onion and garlic for approximately 2 minutes. Add the minced beef. Fry and stir until the meat loosens and is nice and brown. Stir in the sieved tomatoes, diced tomatoes, crumbled stock cube and Italian seasoning and bring to the boil. Cover the pan with its lid and allow the sauce to gently simmer for approximately 10 minutes. Season with cayenne pepper to taste.

3 Arrange the pasta onto deep plates and spoon the Bolognese sauce on the top. Sprinkle with cheese.

Serving suggestion: with a green salad with balsamic dressing.

Tip Suggestions for managing your cooking time:

- Some meals lend themselves perfectly to being prepared in stages. Take for example the Spaghetti Bolognese. You could prepare the sauce with the vegetables and the meat in the morning. In the evening you cook the spaghetti al dente and serve with the warmed up Bolognese sauce.

- Prepare double servings and freeze half.

- Make 2 or 3 savoury pies at a time (depending on the size of your oven) and freeze the extra for later use.

- Always handy to have in your freezer: mixed vegetables (for a quick soup or a stir-fry dish), ready-to-use fish and diced meat, sliced potatoes, minced meat sauces for pasta.

- Handy to have in your fridge for a tasty breakfast or healthy shake: diced ham, strips of bacon, cheese, yoghurt, eggs.

- You can always pre-cook rice, pasta and Chinese noodles and reheat them later in the microwave. After cooking, add a tablespoon of oil to the noodles and pasta to prevent it sticking and clumping together. If the rice, pasta or noodles aren't used at that particular time, it can be easily frozen until a later date.

2. Cooking and sensory disturbances

Sensory disturbances of the skin can often be one of the first symptoms of MS. Sensation in the hands can be diminished or involve tingling, numbness or a burning or electric shock-like pain. You can become clumsier through this lack of feeling, which in turn becomes a problem when preparing food. Meals requiring a lot of slicing and chopping in their preparation become burdensome. That's why this chapter includes recipes that are easy and simple to prepare. These recipes call for little preparation and even less chopping.

Servings are for four persons.

Sweet and sour tilapia with sweet pepper

Preparation time: 10 minutes

2 tablespoons sunflower oil
500 g tilapia fish fillet (firm white fish), in strips
(you can ask the fishmonger to cut the fish in
strips for you)
450 g stir-fry vegetables with sweet pepper
2 tablespoons lemon juice
4 tablespoons ketchup
2 tablespoons sweet chilli sauce
salt and (freshly ground) pepper
boiled rice or Chinese noodles

1 Heat the oil in a wok or frying pan and stir-fry the strips of fish for 1 minute.

2 Add the stir-fry vegetables, lemon juice, ketchup and chilli sauce and stir-fry the ingredients for approximately 4 minutes until the fish is cooked. Add salt and pepper to taste.

3 Serve with boiled rice or Chinese noodles.

Fact Installation of thermostatic taps reduces the risk of scalding by hot tap water. Hang oven gloves next to the microwave/oven and tutor yourself to use them when placing or removing food. If you are suffering from sensory disturbances, an electric can opener and utensils with grips can make your life a lot easier.

Beef broth with Italian vegetables

Preparation time: 10 minutes

1 jar beef stock with meat (350 ml)
1 beef stock cube
250 g Italian stir-fry vegetables
3 sundried tomatoes in oil, drained
salt and (freshly ground) pepper
1 bag garlic croutons

1 Bring a ¹/₂ litre of water to the boil together with the beef stock and stock cube in a soup pan. Add the stir-fry vegetables and cook for 3 minutes until al dente.

2 Cut the tomatoes in thin strips and heat for 1 minute in the soup. Add salt and pepper to the soup to taste.

3 Spoon the broth into bowls and sprinkle with croutons or serve on the side.

Spicy chicken with pineapple and vegetables

Preparation time: 10 minutes

2 tablespoons sunflower oil
1 teaspoon ground ginger
450 g chicken fillet, in strips
250 g Italian stir-fry vegetables
100 g mushrooms, sliced
2 cloves of garlic
1 small tin of pineapple in pieces
100 g bean sprouts
1 tablespoon sweet soy sauce
250 ml cream
salt and (freshly ground) pepper
boiled rice

1 Heat the oil in the wok and add the ground ginger. Cook on a low heat until the ginger starts to scent the air. Stir in the strips of chicken and fry for roughly 2 minutes over high heat until nice and brown. Add the stir-fry vegetables, mushrooms and crushed garlic and cook for 3 minutes.

2 Finally, mix the pineapple, bean sprouts, soy sauce and cream in with the chicken and heat for a further 3 minutes. Add salt and pepper to taste.

3 Serve the strips of chicken with boiled rice.

Fact Don't worry if you have problems sticking to the cooking times. So what if the vegetables are a little too 'al dente' or a bit overcooked. Who cares? As long as you've successfully prepared a hearty and delicious meal for yourself and others. No one will suffer because of a slightly burnt pan.

Pitta bread with chicken and tzatziki

Preparation time: 10 minutes

2 tablespoons sunflower oil
2 tablespoons lemon juice
$1/2$ tablespoon liquid honey
2 cloves of garlic, crushed
3 teaspoons mild ground chilli powder
salt and (freshly ground) pepper
350 g chicken fillet, cut in strips
4 pitta breads
1 tub ready-made tzatziki

1 Mix together the oil, lemon juice, honey, garlic, ground chilli powder and add salt and pepper to taste. Stir the strips of chicken into the marinade.

2 Warm the pitta bread in a toaster

3 In the meantime, heat a non-stick pan and stir-fry the marinated strips of chicken for roughly 5 minutes until cooked and golden brown.

4 Cut the pitta bread open and fill with the chicken mixture. Spoon the tzatziki over the top and serve.

Green tagliatelle with a cream sauce

Preparation time: 10 minutes

500 g green tagliatelle, chilled
250 ml cream
300 g broccoli, small florets
200 g ham strips
salt and (freshly ground) pepper
100 g grated semi-matured cheese
tomato salad

1 Cook the tagliatelle according to the package directions in salt water until al dente.

2 Pour the cream into a pan and add the broccoli. Bring to the boil and allow the broccoli to cook for 4 minutes: purée with an electric mixer. Add the ham strips and heat the sauce for a further 1 minute. Add salt and pepper to taste.

3 Arrange the tagliatelle onto the plates, spoon the cream sauce on top and sprinkle with cheese. Serve with the tomato salad.

Baby potatoes with bacon and broccoli

Preparation time: 15 minutes

120 g smoked bacon, diced
700 g baby potatoes
1 teaspoon thyme
600 g ready-to-cook broccoli
salt and (freshly ground) pepper
2 eggs
4 tablespoons cream

1 Cook the diced bacon for 3 minutes in a pan. Add the baby potatoes and the thyme. Put the lid on the pan and cook for a further 10 minutes. After 5 minutes remove the lid from the pan.

2 In the meantime, boil the broccoli until al dente in salt water for 5 minutes.

3 Beat the eggs lightly together with the cream. Add salt and pepper to taste. Add the mixture to the baby potatoes and allow to simmer on a medium heat.

4 Serve the baby potatoes with the broccoli.

Ratatouille with pangasius fish fillet

Preparation time: 10 minutes

1 carton tomato frito (spicy tomato sauce)
400 g ready-to-cook ratatouille vegetables
1 tablespoon Herbes de Provence
600 g firm white frozen fish, diced roughly in
  chunks 3 cm in size
100 ml dry white wine
salt and (freshly ground) pepper

1 Pour the tomato frito into a pan. Add the vegetables and Herbes de Provence and place the pangasius fish fillet on top. Cover the pan with the lid and bring the sauce to the boil.

2 Turn down the heat and allow the contents to simmer for 5 minutes. Add the wine for the final 2 minutes. Add salt and pepper to taste.

Serving suggestion: with French bread with salted butter.

Tip Cook and bake meals that preferably offer more variety in colours and aromas. As a result you will derive more pleasure from cooking and you will be able to concentrate better.

Stir-fried minced beef with green peas and tomatoes

Preparation time: 15 minutes

2 tablespoons oil
1 onion, chopped
2 cloves of garlic, chopped
1 teaspoon ground ginger
400 g minced beef
1/2 teaspoon cayenne pepper
salt and (freshly ground) pepper
1 tin diced tomatoes (400 g)
250 g frozen peas
1 tablespoon lemon juice
1 tablespoon parsley, finely chopped

1 Heat the oil in a wok or frying pan and stir-fry the onion for roughly 2 minutes. Add the garlic and ground ginger and stir-fry for a further 1 minute. Stir in the minced beef and cayenne pepper and add salt and pepper to taste. Stir-fry the ingredients until the minced beef loosens.

2 Add the tomatoes including the tomato juice, the (frozen) peas and the lemon juice. Bring the ingredients to the boil, then leave covered to simmer for approximately 10 minutes. Sprinkle with parsley.

Serving suggestion: With rice and spinach.

Tip Concentrate on cooking and baking and don't wander off. If the possibility arises where you are able to leave for a few minutes, for example if a dish is gently simmering on the cooker or is already in the oven, set the alarm. It'll alert you to when the food is done.

Savoury quiche with ham and mushrooms

Preparation time: 15 minutes / oven: 45 minutes

500 g mushrooms (from a jar)
6 sundried tomatoes, cut into strips
250 g ham strips
1 tablespoon Italian seasoning
salt and (freshly ground) pepper
3 eggs
3 tablespoons of milk
1 tablespoon liquid margarine
5 slices puff pastry, thawed
1 tablespoon breadcrumbs

1 Preheat the oven to 200 °C.

2 Drain the mushrooms well and mix them together with the tomato strips, ham strips and Italian seasoning. Add salt and pepper to taste.

3 Beat the eggs lightly together with the milk and add to the mushroom mixture.

4 Grease the quiche dish with the margarine and layer the bottom with the pastry slices. Use a fork to prick the pastry base, then sprinkle with breadcrumbs. Spread the mushroom mixture evenly into the quiche dish.

5 Bake the quiche in the middle of the oven for 30-40 minutes until golden brown and cooked.

Sauerkraut with scrambled eggs and hash browns

Preparation time: 15 minutes

50 g chorizo
3 tablespoons oil
1 pack hash browns (frozen)
1 pack (seasoned) sauerkraut
2 eggs
2 tablespoons of milk
salt and (freshly ground) pepper

1 Cut the chorizo into bite-size pieces

2 Heat 2 tablespoons of oil in a pan and cook the potato cakes for 6-8 minutes until golden brown.

3 Place the sauerkraut in a pan containing a layer of water and cook on a medium heat.

4 Beat the eggs lightly together with the milk and add salt and pepper to taste. Heat the remainder of the oil in a large pan, add the egg mixture and stir until the egg is cooked. Mix the warm sauerkraut and chorizo in with the cooked eggs and heat for a further 2 minutes.

Serve the sauerkraut with the hash browns.

3. Seafood recipes

Fish is well-known to be a healthy food choice. This is chiefly due to the rich source of omega-3 fatty acids found in fish. Omega-3s are smooth fats, the so-called polyunsaturated fatty acids, meaning they are fluid at room temperature and can remain fluid-like at temperatures approaching freezing. Our brains consist largely of structural fats. Omega-3s fatty acids are crucial for the normal development and optimal growth of the brain. To ensure the average recommended daily uptake of omega-3, you are advised to eat at least two portions of fish (approximately 100-150 gram) a week, including one portion of oily fish. According to the UK Food Standards Authority, this is the best way to help you obtain sufficient omega-3 fatty acids. However, more than two portions of fish per week is of little or no additional benefit. Examples of oily fish are herring, salmon, sardines, anchovies and mackerel.

Fish, however, is not only a rich source of omega-3, but it contains other essential nutrients as well, such as proteins, vitamins (especially vitamin D) and minerals. Vitamin D seems to have a beneficial influence on the immune systems of those suffering from multiple sclerosis. Servings are for four persons.

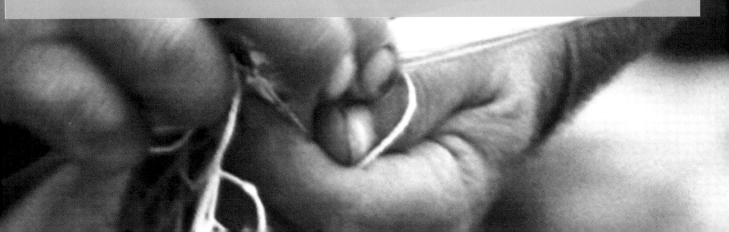

Pasta shells with sardines and lemon cream sauce

Preparation time: 15 minutes

1 carton crème fraîche (125 ml)
3 tablespoons capers, coarsely chopped
Grated rind of 1 lemon
2 tablespoons basil leaves, coarsely chopped
salt and (freshly ground) pepper
300 g dried pasta shells (conchiglie)
1 tin anchovies, drained and cut into strips
4 tablespoons oil
12 small fresh sardines (cleaned)

1 Mix the crème fraîche in a bowl together with the capers, lemon rind and basil leaves. Add salt and pepper to taste.

2 Cook the pasta according to the package directions in salt water until al dente, then allow the pasta to drain in a colander.

3 Mix the lemon cream sauce (step 1) and the anchovies into the pasta and gently heat.

4 In the meantime, heat the oil in a non-stick pan and cook the sardines for roughly 5 minutes until golden brown. Halfway through, turn the sardines gently over.

5 Arrange the pasta onto four plates. Place the sardines on top. Sprinkle with pepper.

Serving suggestion: with tomato salad.

Baked salmon in a creamy garlic-herb sauce
Preparation time: 15 minutes

600 g salmon fillet, preferably a thick piece
salt and (freshly ground) pepper
4 tablespoons finely chopped parsley
4 tablespoons finely chopped chervil
2 tablespoons finely chopped tarragon
2 tablespoons finely chopped dill
100 g butter
2 cloves of garlic, peeled
10 tablespoons crème fraîche
2 tablespoons lemon juice

1   Flavour the salmon with salt and pepper, rubbing in well. Cut the fillet crossways in strips roughly 3 cm wide. Mix the herbs together in a deep plate and roll the salmon strips through the seasoning, coating thoroughly.

2   Melt the butter in a non-stick pan and squeeze the garlic of its essence above it; cook the garlic for approximately 30 seconds. Add the salmon and cook on a medium heat for roughly 5 minutes until light brown and cooked; turn every so often.

3   Arrange the fish onto the plates. Mix the crème fraîche in with the leftover fat in the pan and bring to the boil while stirring. Add lemon juice and salt and pepper to taste. Spoon the sauce over the salmon.

Serving suggestion: with boiled baby potatoes (with the skin) and a mixed salad.

Provencal mackerel on French bread

Preparation time: 20 minutes

2 tomatoes
100 g mackerel fillet
1/2 red sweet pepper, cut into pieces
75 g seedless black olives, coarsely chopped
2 spring onions, cut in narrow rings
1 tablespoon olive oil
2 teaspoons lemon juice
(freshly ground) pepper
16 pieces of French bread, sliced at an angle
75 g semi-matured cheese (slices)

1 Quarter the tomatoes, remove the juice and the seeds and dice the flesh. Cut the mackerel into pieces, remove any fish bones.

2 Purée the tomato, mackerel, sweet pepper, olives and spring onions with an electric mixer or in a food processor; the mixture is still somewhat coarse. Stir in the oil and the lemon juice and add salt and pepper to taste.

3 Layer the slices of French bread with the cheese and spread the mackerel on top.

Fish wrapped in cured ham with basil sauce

Preparation time: 30 minutes

250 g firm fish fillet (monkfish or tilapia)
salt and (freshly ground) pepper
4 slices of cured ham
30 g basil, coarsely chopped
2 tablespoons wine- or balsamic vinegar
2 teaspoons mustard
1 teaspoon sugar
1 clove of garlic, peeled
200 ml cream, light
40 g butter
5 cherry tomatoes, quartered

1 Cut the fish into approximately 12 pieces of equal size and sprinkle with salt and pepper. Cut the slices of ham into 3 long strips and wrap around the pieces of fish; prick the ham-wrapped fish with a cocktail stick to hold everything in place.

2 Place the basil, vinegar, mustard and sugar into a mixing bowl and squeeze the garlic of its essence above it. Add the cream and purée the contents with an electric mixer or in the food processor. Add salt and pepper to taste. Pour the mixture into a saucepan.

3 Heat the butter in a non-stick pan and cook the ham-wrapped fish for roughly 6 minutes until light brown all over. Thoroughly heat the sauce in the saucepan, stir occasionally.

4 Spoon the sauce onto plates the sit the fish on the plate (remove the cocktail stick). Arrange the tomatoes around the plates and serve.

Baked sole with shrimp

Preparation time: 25 minutes

8 small filleted sole (flat fish), ready to cook
salt
2 lemons
300 ml milk
6 tablespoons flour
60 g butter
150 g small shrimps
a few sprigs of parsley

1 Pat the soles dry with a paper towel and flavour the fish with salt and pepper, rub in well. Leave t infuse for approximately 10 minutes.

2 Squeeze the juice from one lemon; cut the other in half, then the halves into quarters. Pour the milk into a deep plate and sprinkle flour onto another flat plate. Dredge the soles first in the milk, allow to drain, then roll into the flour. Shake off the excess.

3 Heat half the quantity of the butter in a non-stick pan and cook 4 of the soles for roughly 5 minute until golden brown; turn the fish halfway. Remove the fish from the pan and wrap in aluminium foil to preserve the heat. Cook the remaining 4 soles in the rest of the butter.

4 Add the lemon juice and shrimp to the leftover fa in the pan. Heat for roughly 30 seconds and stir well.

5 Arrange the fish onto plates and spoon the shrimp on top. Garnish with segments of lemon and finish off with parsley.

Serving suggestion: with tomato salad and chips.

Fish-leek oven-bake dish

Preparation time: 25 minutes / oven: 25 minutes

2 tablespoons liquid margarine
1 onion, chopped
2 cloves of garlic, finely chopped
500 g chopped leek
4 tablespoons pesto
250 ml cream
salt and (freshly ground) pepper
600 g fish fillet (cod or haddock)
2 tablespoons lemon juice

1 Preheat the oven to 220 °C. Heat the margarine in a wok or frying pan and gently cook the onion for approximately 3 minutes. Add the garlic and the leek and stir-fry the ingredients for roughly 4 minutes.

2 Stir the pesto and cream in with the leek and add salt and pepper to season.

3 Cut the fish into pieces of roughly 4 cm in size, drizzle with lemon juice and sprinkle with salt and pepper.

4 Transfer the leek mixture into an oven dish and spoon the fish in. Cover the dish with aluminium foil, place on a grid in the middle of the oven and leave for approximately 25 minutes to cook.

Serving suggestion: with tagliatelle or boiled potatoes.

Sea bass fillets with cheese-onion crust

Preparation time: 10 minutes / oven: 20 minutes

4 sea bass fillets (cod) each 200 g
1 tablespoon lemon juice
salt and (freshly ground) pepper
2 tablespoons olive oil
2 onions, chopped
2 cloves of garlic, finely chopped
2 teaspoons Herbes de Provence
1 tablespoon liquid margarine
50 g white bread crumbs
30 g grated mature (Gouda) cheese
lemon segments

1 Drizzle the fish fillets with lemon juice and sprinkle with salt and pepper. Grease an oven dish with roughly $1/2$ a tablespoon of oil, then place the fish fillets side by side in the dish.

2 Preheat the oven to 190 °C. Heat the remainder of the oil in a pan and gently cook the onion for approximately 5 minutes until golden brown. Add the garlic and the seasoning and cook for a further 1 minute, stirring well. Spread the onion mixture evenly over the fish.

3 Use the same pan in which the onions were cooked and heat the margarine. Do not allow the margarine to turn brown. Stir in the bread crumbs. Remove the pan from the heat before adding the cheese. Spread the bread-cheese mixture evenly over the fish.

4 Put the dish on a grid in the middle of the oven and leave for 20 minutes to cook until golden brown. Remove the dish from the oven and garnish the fish with the lemon segments.

Serving suggestion: with French beans and mashed potato.

Thai fish curry

Preparation time: 25 minutes

600 g fish fillet (cod or tilapia)
2 limes
250 g mushrooms
2-3 tablespoons Thai green curry paste
1 tin coconut milk
2 tablespoons Thai fish sauce (nam plah)
3 tablespoons soy sauce
6 spring onions, cut into narrow rings
3 tablespoons finely chopped coriander
3 tablespoons finely chopped basil

1 Cut the fish fillets into pieces of roughly 4 cm in size. Squeeze the juice of one lime onto the fish, cut the other lime into slices. Clean and quarter the mushrooms.

2 Heat the curry paste in a wok or frying pan, stirring continuously. Add the coconut milk and bring the ingredients to the boil, all the while stirring. Add the lime slices and the mushrooms, then mix in the fish- and soy sauce. Allow the sauce to gently simmer for 3 minutes.

3 Add the pieces of fish and spring onion to the coconut mixture and allow the fish to cook for approximately 6 minutes. Sprinkle the dish with coriander and basil.

Serving suggestion: with rice and cucumber salad.

Pasta salad with sweet pepper, tuna fish and olives

Preparation time: 40 minutes

2 red sweet peppers
350 g conchiglie (medium-sized pasta shells)
2 tablespoons olive oil
2 cloves of garlic, chopped
1 tablespoon fresh thyme leaves
50 g rocket
1 small tin of tuna fish in water, drained
50 g seedless black olives
sea salt and (freshly ground) pepper
50 g Parmesan cheese curls, coarse

Tip   Learning a new recipe? Make use of a quiet moment during the day to try it out instead of waiting until dinner time when everyone is home and hungry.

1 Place the sweet peppers for approximately 20 minutes under a hot grill until completely scorched. Then, put them in a plastic bag and leave sealed for 10 minutes. Remove the skin and the seeds. Cut the flesh into bite-size pieces.

2 Cook the pasta according to the package directions in salt water until al dente. Heat the oil in a pan and cook the garlic for 1 minute on a medium flame. Add the sweet pepper and thyme and gently heat.

3 Tear the larger rocket leaves into small pieces. Drain the pasta. Add to it the sweet pepper, tuna, rocket and olives. Add salt and pepper to taste.

4 Serve the salad at room temperature and sprinkle with the cheese curls.

Serving suggestion: with crispy, warm bread.

Salted herring sauce

Preparation time: 10 minutes

1 egg, hardboiled
125 ml crème fraîche
3 salted herrings, cut into small pieces
1 onion, chopped very fine
1 large sweet sour gherkin, chopped very fine
4 slices pumpernickel (rye bread) or white bread

1 Peel the egg and slice it in half. Remove the yolk. Cut the egg white into small pieces. Mash the yolk in a bowl and mix with the crème fraîche.

2 Add the herring, onion, pickle and egg white and stir the ingredients well.

3 Spoon the chopped herring sauce onto the rye- or white bread.

4. Cooking and heat sensitivity

Heat intolerance (heat sensitivity) is a common issue for people living with MS. It is an aggravating factor that can also temporarily worsen MS symptoms. It manifests itself by an increase in body temperature as a result of exertion or a rise in the temperature of the surroundings. Common symptoms are mounting fatigue, blurred vision or muscle weakness. The symptoms can become exacerbated during exercise or sport, after taking a warm bath or a long journey in a warm car, but also during relentlessly warm summers.

By adjusting your diet you can possibly reduce the effects of heat on your symptoms. On hot, sunny days, it's better to have five or six light meals spread throughout the day. During the winter months your vitamin D blood level is usually at its lowest. In the medical literature circulating in the year 2000, Vitamin D was constantly referred to as a 'natural inhibitor' of MS. Other research shows that Vitamin D blood levels are lower than normal during a relapse and in MS sufferers with limited mobility, and that taking Vitamin D supplements can help prevent the development of new inflammation or lesions.

This chapter includes light, refreshing recipes.

Servings are for four persons.

Dutch rusk with low-sugar marmalade, apple and crunchy muesli

Preparation time: 10 minutes

2 small apples
4 baker's rusks (dry biscuits)
2 tablespoons skimmed cream cheese
2 tablespoons low-sugar marmalade
2 tablespoons crunchy muesli

1 Wash and clean the apples. Remove the core and cut into segments.

2 Spread some cream cheese on the rusks and top with low-sugar marmalade.

3 Layer the rusks with segments of apple and sprinkle with crunchy muesli.

Whole-wheat cupcakes with tutti-frutti

Preparation time: 15 minutes / oven: 35 minutes

100 g tutti-frutti (chopped candied fruit)
125 g butter at room temperature
125 g caster sugar
lemon juice
salt
2 eggs at room temperature
80 g whole-wheat flour
45 g self-raising flour
1 tablespoon milk or ginger syrup
12 paper cupcake forms

1 Preheat the oven to 150 °C. Chop the tutti-frutti into small pieces.

2 Whisk the butter together with the sugar, lemon juice and salt until soft and creamy.

3 Add the eggs one at a time and stir until smooth, light and fluffy.

4 Sieve the whole-wheat flour and self-raising flour and gradually blend into the batter mix. Stir in the milk and the chopped tutti-frutti.

5 Divide the batter into the 12 cupcake forms and place in the oven to cook for approximately 35 minutes until golden brown. To check their readiness insert a thin skewer into the centre of the cupcake; if the skewer is sticky, the cupcakes aren't yet cooked.

Pasta salad with green beans and salmon

Preparation time: 25 minutes

250 g noodles
150 g green beans, halved
salt and (freshly ground) pepper
200 g smoked salmon
50 g hazelnuts
1/2 lemon
2-3 sprigs of basil
3 tablespoons extra virgin olive oil
100 ml full-fat yoghurt
3 tomatoes, skinned and cut into strips
75 g rocket (rucola)

1 Cook the pasta according to the package directions in salt water until al dente.

2 Cook the green beans in salt water for approximately 5-7 minutes until al dente. Then rinse off in a colander under cold running water and allow to drain well.

3 Cut half the salmon into small pieces and the rest into broad strips. Coarsely chop the hazelnuts and roast in a dry pan until golden brown. Allow to cool.

4 Wipe the lemon clean and finely grate the zest. Squeeze the juice from the lemon. Finely chop the basil and add it to a bowl with the lemon juice, grated zest, oil and yoghurt to make the dressing. Add salt and pepper to taste.

5 Drain the pasta. Stir into the dressing while still warm. Spoon in the green beans, tomatoes and pieces of salmon. Allow the salad to cool.

6 Mix the nuts and the rocket into the salad, garnish with the strips of salmon and serve.

Brown crusted roll with tuna fish salad

Preparation time: 15 minutes

1 tin of natural tuna fish (drained weight
   70 gram)
2 sun-dried tomatoes in oil, drained
20 seedless green olives
4 tablespoons Greek yoghurt
salt and (freshly ground) pepper
4 brown crusted rolls
20 g low-fat butter
40 g lamb's lettuce

1 Drain the tuna fish well.

2 Finely chop the sun-dried tomatoes and cut the olives into small pieces. Mix in with the tuna fish. Add the yoghurt and salt and pepper to taste.

3 Halve and butter the crusted rolls. Divide half of the lamb's lettuce onto one half of the crusted rolls, spoon some of the tuna fish mixture on top and finish off with the remaining lamb's lettuce. Top with the other half of the roll.

Gazpacho with spicy yoghurt

Preparation time: 30 minutes / interval: 3 hours

3 slices of white bread, with crusts removed

2 cloves of garlic, chopped

4 tablespoons olive oil

2 tablespoons red wine vinegar

5 firm tomatoes, diced

50 ml orange juice

400 g cucumber, diced

2 red sweet peppers, diced

2 red onions, chopped

salt and (freshly ground) pepper

125 ml plain yoghurt

1/2 teaspoon ground dry chili flakes

1/2 teaspoon ground cumin

1 Place the bread in a bowl together with the garlic, oil and vinegar. Mix together and leave to infuse.

2 Purée the bread mixture, tomatoes, orange juice and half of the cucumber, sweet peppers and onion in a food processor. Sieve the mixture above a bowl. Add salt and pepper to taste and place the bowl of extracted soup in the fridge for 3 hours.

3 Whisk the yoghurt, ground chili flakes, cumin and a pinch of salt together. Remove the soup from the fridge and ladle into soup bowls. Garnish the soup with the remaining vegetables and finish off with a dollop of spicy yoghurt.

Samphire salad with citrus fruit and pineapple

Preparation time: 35 minutes

1 fresh pineapple, peeled
1 yellow grapefruit
1 orange
1 teaspoon sesame oil
1 teaspoon walnut oil
3 tablespoons sunflower oil
1 tablespoon mustard
1 tablespoon white wine vinegar
salt and (freshly ground) pepper
200 g samphire
45 g shaved almonds, roasted

1 Cut in the pineapple in slices of roughly 1 1/2 cm. Remove the core using either a corer or a knife. Preheat the grill.

2 Peel the grapefruit and orange by cutting away the skin, pith and membrane around the flesh. Collect the escaping juice. Cut the citrus segments in half.

3 Whisk the oil, mustard, vinegar and collected citrus juice together. Add salt and pepper to the dressing to taste.

4 Place the pineapple slices in an oven dish and coat lightly with the dressing. Grill the pineapple until the edges turn brown. Turn the pineapple over, coat again lightly with the dressing and grill. Cut the pineapple into pieces. The resulting pineapple juice can be added to the dressing.

5 Cook the glasswort in a pan with salt water for roughly 4 minutes until al dente. Rinse the glasswort off in cold water and allow to drain in a colander.

6 Mix the glasswort, grapefruit, orange and pineapple together. Add the dressing and sprinkle with almonds.

Tropical fruit salad with crunchy muesli

Preparation time: 10 minutes

1 mango
1 banana
1 pear
1 small tin of pineapple in pieces
1 tin lychees
100 g crunchy muesli with coconut
400 ml vanilla yoghurt

Tip   Keep your work surface, as your kitchen, uncluttered, clean and tidy.

1 Peel the mango, remove the pit and dice. Peel the banana and cut into slices. Peel the pear, remove the core and dice. Drain the pineapple and retain the juice. Drain the lychees.

2 Mix two tablespoons of pineapple juice in a bowl with the mango, banana, pear, pineapple and lychees.

3 Arrange the salad onto four plates, sprinkle muesli over the fruit and spoon the yoghurt on top.

Ice-cold apple mousse with cinnamon

Preparation time: 5 minutes

1 large jar of apple sauce
8 scoops of vanilla ice cream
1-2 teaspoons of ground cinnamon

1 Purée the apple sauce together with the ice cream and ground cinnamon with an electric mixer or in a food processor until the ingredients are light and fluffy.

2 Divide the mousse into 4 glasses.

Tip Substitute your apple sauce with apricot- or rhubarb compote.

Mexican corn salad

Preparation time: 20 minutes

1 cucumber
1 avocado
juice of 1 lime
2 tablespoons olive oil
dried chilli pepper using a pepper mill
2 teaspoons dried oregano
salt and (freshly ground) pepper
1 small red onion, chopped
250 g cherry tomatoes, halved
1 tin of corn (300 gram)
15 g finely chopped coriander

1 Halve the cucumber, remove the seeds and sap, then dice. Peel the avocado and dice.

2 Whisk the lime juice in a bowl with the olive oil, freshly ground chilli pepper and oregano to make the dressing. Add salt and pepper to taste.

3 Stir in the onion, cucumber, avocado, tomato, corn and coriander.

Serving suggestion: with warm tortillas, steak tartare and piquant salsa.

Grilled steak with snow pea salad

Preparation time: 20 minutes

150 g snow peas
1 small courgette
100 g young leaf lettuce
30 g rocket (rucola)
1 tablespoon white wine vinegar
1 teaspoon mustard
3 tablespoons cold vegetable stock (from a
   stock cube)
salt and (freshly ground) pepper
4 steaks, roughly 100 g
1 tablespoon sunflower oil

1 Cook the snow peas in salt water for 3 minutes until al dente. Drain and rinse under cold water. Again drain well.

2 Cut the courgette in half, remove the seeds and slice in narrow arcs. Mix the courgette in a bowl with the leaf lettuce, rocket and snow peas.

3 Whisk the vinegar with the mustard and add the vegetable stock. Add salt and pepper to the dressing to taste, then mix into the salad.

4 Coat both sides of the steaks lightly with oil. Heat the grill pan. Place the steaks in the pan and cook both sides on a high heat for 2 minutes. Sprinkle the steaks with salt and pepper and serve with the snow pea salad.

Serving suggestion: with hash browns or boiled potatoes.

Spicy steamed vegetables with steak tartare in yoghurt

Preparation time: 15 minutes

1 l vegetable stock
200 g shredded oxheart cabbage
200 g leek, in rings
100 g bean sprouts
1/2 chilli pepper, cut into small pieces
300 g steak tartare
salt and (freshly ground) pepper
1 clove of garlic, crushed
1 tablespoon olive oil
200 ml low-fat yoghurt
2 tablespoons finely chopped coriander

1 Bring the vegetable stock to boil in a (steamer) pan. Place the vegetables and chilli pepper in the food steamer or large steel cooking sieve. Cover the pan and steam the vegetables for 6 minutes.

2 Mix the steak tartare with salt, pepper and garlic. Create 12 balls and flatten lightly.

3 Heat the oil in a pan and cook the meatballs on both sides for 2 minutes.

4 Mix the yoghurt with the coriander and add salt and pepper to taste.

5 Spoon the vegetables into a dish and arrange the tartar meatballs on top. Serve with the yoghurt on the side.

Serving suggestion: with basmati rice.

Imperial chicken and rice

Preparation time: 35 minutes

500 g chicken fillet, in 4 pieces
cayenne pepper
salt
3 tablespoons olive oil
1 onion, finely chopped
1 clove of garlic, finely chopped
75 g pine nuts
325 g basmati rice
1 tin of diced tomatoes (400 g)
75 g raisins
2 chicken stock cubes
4 tablespoons finely chopped dill

1 Flavour the chicken fillets with cayenne pepper and salt to taste, rub in well. Heat 2 tablespoons of oil in a pan and cook the chicken fillets, browning them quickly all over. Remove the chicken fillets from the pan.

2 Heat the rest of the oil in the same pan and sauté the onions, garlic and pine nuts, keep stirring until lightly browned. Add the rice, cook for 3 minutes while stirring. Pour in the diced tomatoes including the tomato juice. Add the raisins, chicken stock cubes, 600 ml of hot water and the dill. Keep stirring and bring the ingredients to the boil.

3 Place the chicken fillets on top of the rice and cover the pan with its lid. Cook the rice on a low heat for approximately 20 minutes. Remove the pan from the heat and cover with a clean tea towel. Allow the rice dish to steam dry for 10 minutes.

Mint yoghurt with white grapes

Preparation time: 15 minutes

8 mint leaves (+ extra)
150 ml low fat yoghurt
125 ml (semi-skimmed) crème fraîche
4 walnuts (peeled)
500 g seedless grapes
2 tablespoons sugar
1/2 teaspoon cinnamon

1 Cut the mint into thin strips. Whisk the yoghurt with the crème fraîche. Add the mint. Coarsely chop the nuts and roast in a dry pan. Wash the grapes and remove from the bunch.

2 Serve the minted yoghurt with the grapes. Sprinkle with the walnuts, sugar and cinnamon and garnish the dessert with mint.

Buttermilk pudding with strawberry salsa

Preparation time: 20 minutes / interval: 2 hours

8 leaves of white gelatine
juice and grated zest of 3 limes
100 g sugar
400 ml buttermilk
butter to grease the ramekins
500 g strawberries
1 tablespoon finely chopped fresh mint

1 Soak the gelatine in cold water. In a pan, bring to the boil 50 ml of water and the juice and grated zest of 1 ½ limes. Squeeze the gelatine leaves well to remove excess water. Remove the liquor from the heat and add the gelatine. Stir until the gelatine dissolves. Add the sugar and stir until the sugar too dissolves. Allow to cool, and add the buttermilk. Let the mixture cool some more until it become gelatinous.

2 Grease the ramekins, pudding moulds or cups (volume roughly 125 ml) and fill with the pudding mixture. Leave in the fridge for approximately 1-2 hours.

3 In the meantime, wash the strawberries, remove the tops and cut into pieces. Mix the strawberries in a bowl with the rest of the grated lime rind, mint and 1 tablespoon of lime juice. Leave to infuse for half an hour.

4 Place a plate on top of the ramekin, pudding mould or cup and turn upside down. Spoon the strawberry salsa over the top.

5. Budget meals

A chronic illness brings with it several additional costs. This chapter shows how, even with a limited budget, you can prepare something appetising every day. The trick is to cook delicious meals with affordable ingredients.

Servings are for 4 persons.

Cajun wraps

Preparation time: 15 minutes

300 g chicken fillet
2 tablespoons Cajun seasoning
4 tablespoons flour
2 eggs, loosely whipped
100 g breadcrumbs
knob of butter
4 tortillas
125 ml sour cream
8 slices of bacon, fried in their own fat
80 g iceberg lettuce, cut thinly into strips
2 tablespoons spring onion, cut thinly in rings

Tip   Cook large portions of dishes that can be frozen; cook once, eat twice.

What to do with leftovers?

● Leftover boiled potatoes: mix in a salad with herring and beetroot, bake in the oven with cheese and tomatoes, make potato cakes or

1 Place the chicken fillets one by one between two sheets of aluminium foil and tenderise (pound) with the underside of a skillet or pan. Flavour the chicken fillets with the Cajun seasoning, rub in well.

2 Sprinkle flour onto one plate, pour the eggs onto another and the breadcrumbs onto a third. Roll the chicken fillets in the flour (shake off the excess), dredge in the egg then roll in the breadcrumbs.

3 Melt the butter on a medium heat in a pan and cook the chicken fillets for 3 minutes on both sides until golden brown. Remove onto a cutting board and slice into strips. Warm the tortillas for a couple of seconds in a preheated pan.

4 Coat the tortillas with sour cream. Layer with the bacon, lettuce and spring onion. Arrange the chicken strips on top and roll the tortillas gently to enclose the filling.

Sweet chicken fillet with peach and rice
Preparation time: 15 minutes

350 g rice
1 onion, chopped
1 clove of garlic, finely chopped
2 tablespoons oil
400 g chicken fillet, cut into pieces
1 tin peaches (approximately 400 g)
1 small tin of tomato purée
salt and (freshly ground) pepper

1 Cook the rice according to the package directions.

2 Sauté the onion and garlic in the oil. Add the chicken pieces and cook for approximately 8 minutes.

3 Drain the peaches and retain the juice. Cut the peaches into pieces. Add these, the tomato purée and 5 tablespoons of peach juice to the chicken. Stir well. Cover the pan with its lid and allow to gently simmer for 5 minutes. Add salt and pepper to taste.

use as a topping for an oven-baked dish.

● Pasta: mix in a salad with tomatoes and pesto, with boiled vegetables in an oven-baked dish or in soup as a substitute for vermicelli.

● Rice: mix in a salad with chicken, curry, pineapple and yoghurt; make Indonesian fried rice, rice pudding or rice cakes.

● Vegetables: make a farmer's omelette, vegetable soup or use to fill puff pastry pockets or as nibbles in a sauce dip.

● Meat/fish: great for making sandwiches, a ragout, salad or an oven-baked dish with leftover vegetables and potatoes.

Savoury bread oven-baked dish

Preparation time: 10 minutes / oven: 20 minutes

1 tablespoon oil
2 onions, chopped
150 g bacon strips
1 teaspoon tarragon
1 tablespoon honey
8 slices white sesame bread, diced
6 beef tomatoes, seedless, cut into pieces
salt and (freshly grounded) pepper
100 g semi-matured cheese, grated

1 Preheat the oven to 180 °C.

2 Heat the oil in a pan and sauté the onions with the strips of bacon and tarragon for 3 minutes. Add the honey to the mix. Stir well.

3 Blend the bread, tomatoes and bacon mixture in a large bowl. Add salt and pepper to taste.

4 Transfer the mixture into an oven dish and sprinkle with the grated cheese. Place the dish in the oven to cook for 20 minutes until golden brown.

Serving suggestion: with lamb's lettuce salad.

Tip Shopping wisely is an important part of 'budget' meals. Preferably shop once a week; plan a weekly menu and shop accordingly. Purchase only food that is on offer, which you already use and is non-perishable. Eating food in season is also a good way to save money. Larger quantities are very tempting to buy, but if only half the product gets used by its expiration date then the rest will be thrown away.

Summer club sandwich

Preparation time: 20 minutes

1 tablespoon olive oil
1 courgette, cut at an angle
100 g chorizo, slices
12 slices white bread
100 g sliced cured ham
1 melon, thinly sliced
150 g feta cheese, thinly sliced
2 tomatoes, sliced
4 tablespoons basil, coarsely chopped

Tip Do your shopping after you've had a meal. You're apt to be a little more impulsive in your purchase if you're hungry or feeling peckish. There are various different types of meat and fish that are inexpensive and still very tasty (remember: smaller portions).

1 Heat the oil in a pan and cook the courgette for 2 minutes on both sides. Remove the courgette from the pan and allow to drain on kitchen paper. Now put the chorizo in the pan and cook for 1 minute on both sides.

2 Toast the bread.

3 To make the sandwich, stack as follows: slice of bread, courgette, chorizo, another slice of bread, cured ham, melon, feta cheese, tomato, basil and another slice of bread. Cut the club sandwich diagonally in half and spear with a cocktail skewer.

4 Serve.

Curried-cream fish on a bed of cabbage

Preparation time: 10 minutes / oven: 30 minutes

1 tablespoon oil
250 g white cabbage, cut thinly into strips
$^{1}/_{2}$ teaspoon ground paprika
250 ml cooking cream
1 $^{1}/_{2}$ tablespoons curry powder
3 tablespoons parsley, chopped
salt and (freshly ground) pepper
500 g white fish fillet (e.g. pollock, haddock or tilapia)
2 tomatoes, seedless, cut into strips
2 stalks of celery, cut into arcs
50 g mature cheese, grated

1 Heat the oven to 200 °C

2 Heat the oil in a pan and (stir-) fry the cabbage together with the ground paprika for approximately 4 minutes. Mix the cream with the curry, 2 $^{1}/_{2}$ tablespoons of parsley, salt and pepper.

3 Transfer the cabbage into a large oven dish. Place the fish on top and sprinkle with salt and pepper. Layer with the tomatoes and celery. Pour the cream over the entire dish and finish off with a sprinkling of grated cheese.

4 Cover the dish with aluminium foil and put in the oven for 30 minutes. Remove the aluminium foil after 15 minutes.

5 Garnish with the remaining parsley.

Serving suggestion: with mashed potatoes.

Fish from Curaçao

Preparation time: 45 minutes / marinate: 1 hour

3 cloves of garlic
3 limes, squeezed
3 spring onions, finely chopped
salt and (freshly ground) pepper
500 g white fish fillet (e.g. pollock, tilapia)
4 tablespoons flour
2 tablespoons liquid margarine
1 onion, finely chopped
1 chilli pepper, in rings
6 (plum) tomatoes, peeled and finely chopped

1 Finely chop 2 cloves of garlic. Mix the lime juice, spring onion and1 crushed garlic clove together. Add salt and pepper to taste. Pour the marinade over the fish, cover and allow to marinate for 1 hour in the fridge.

2 Preheat the oven to 100 °C.

3 Take the fish out of the marinade, pat dry and cut into pieces. Roll the fish in the flour. Heat the margarine in a frying pan and cook the fish until it's nice and brown and crisp. Transfer to an oven dish and keep warm in the oven.

4 Sauté the onion with the rest of the garlic and chilli pepper in the leftover fat until golden brown. Add the tomatoes and allow to simmer for 20 minutes.

5 Add salt and pepper to the sauce to taste and serve with the fish.

Serving suggestion: with rice and baked sweet plantains.

Classic pancakes filled with baked cinnamon apples

Preparation time: 20 minutes

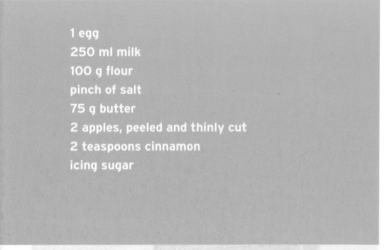

1 egg
250 ml milk
100 g flour
pinch of salt
75 g butter
2 apples, peeled and thinly cut
2 teaspoons cinnamon
icing sugar

1 Beat the eggs lightly together with the milk. Add the flour and mix until the batter is smooth. Pour in the rest of the milk and add the salt. Stir, again, until the batter is smooth.

2 Heat a pan and add a knob of butter. Cook 4 pancakes and keep warm in the oven or wrap in aluminium foil.

3 Sprinkle the apple slices with cinnamon. Melt the rest of the butter in the pan and cook the apple slices for approximately 2 minutes on both sides.

4 Arrange the pancakes onto 4 plates and divide the apples evenly. Fold the pancakes as you would an envelope. Sprinkle with icing sugar and serve.

Any type of fruit can be used in fruit pancakes, for example baked pears, oranges and nectarines.

Fact It's cheaper in the long run if you store vegetables and fruit properly. Most fleshy vegetables such as tomatoes, cucumber and courgettes are best kept in cool, dry dark places rather than being refrigerated.

6. MS and dysphagia

Eating and drinking with others is such a common occurrence that we don't overly dwell on. Even a slight clearing of the throat or full-blown coughing fit on occasion isn't viewed as anything out of the ordinary. A healthy body is equipped to handle excessive eating and drinking. However, it's prudent to take the time to enjoy and visually savour the taste/aroma and presentation of what is set before you. Unfortunately, for many people, enjoyment of food and drink isn't as straightforward as it seems. This also applies to people with MS.

Our swallowing mechanism is in fact coordinated by a network of nerves that are controlled by a specific part of the brain, the brain stem. With the onset of MS, damage to these nerves or damage to the brain stem itself can gradually produce changes in swallowing. This can lead to problems in swallowing or dysphagia.

Between 30-50 % of sufferers from MS may develop a mild to severe form of dysphagia. The problems tend to arise in later stages of the disease. An occasional clearing of the throat after a drink or a cough during dinner is seldom considered choking. This is also apparent with MS. Yet, these are signs that the swallowing reflex is functioning less than optimally. Where does the line between healthy and aberrant swallowing lie? When should a person with MS start to worry?

It becomes worrisome when the clearing of the throat and the coughing occur more frequently than is normal. It becomes worrisome with the onset of pneumonia. In these situations diagnostic evaluation of swallowing can help provide answers to the cause or dispel any assumptions. Diagnostic evaluation can lead to effective swallowing techniques and therapies, but more on that later.

What is distinctive with MS is that the swallowing mechanism can sharply deteriorate after an attack or relapse. However, from clinical observations, we also know it can gradually recover to levels before the relapse. Swallowing techniques can be used in the recovery stage (for example by modifying, then gradually normalising consistencies, quantity per bite, swallow rate, allocated time, thickening of diluted fluid, help with fluid/food intake, verbal cues etc.). Increased vigilance and awareness from attending health care professionals acts as a supportive and preventive net.

With MS, subtle swallowing problems during eating and drinking can increase in frequency. Dysphagia can be extremely diverse in nature. Below is a description of the most common swallowing problems associated with MS, namely:
- the inability to regulate the food bolus with each sip of drink, resulting in large quantities of fluid diluting the food;
- a weakening of the muscles in the face and tongue whereby chewing requires a much greater effort;
- during or after swallowing from diluted fluid, clearing of the throat or coughing due to a delayed swallowing reflex while fluid passes from the mouth to deep in the throat;
- choking on own saliva;
- during or after a meal, clearing of the throat or coughing due to weakening muscles in the throat wall whereby food particles remain lodged in the throat;
- increased difficulty in use of the tongue to manoeuvre food to the back of the mouth. It becomes more difficult to swallow;
- after swallowing, food can return to the throat resulting in clearing of the throat/coughing;
- frustrating dryness in the mouth due to lack of saliva production;
- reduced sensitivity in the throat and airway whereby the cough reflex becomes inactive during choking;

- aspiration of fluid/food (into the airway) without realisation;
- real danger of suffocation (an exception)

Fortunately, there are many treatment- and rehabilitation centres now with specialised speech/language pathologists (SLP) who offer support. Within many hospitals swallowing teams can be consulted to review symptoms objectively.

The change from normal to aberrant swallowing in sufferers with MS can develop subtly over a period of years. It commonly starts with coughing and/or a sensation of something being lodged in the throat. Using knowledge of the mechanics of swallowing and how MS affects swallowing, we can, for example with better precepts and more awareness of food/drink, offer MS patients preventive support. Maintaining an independent and safe approach to food/drink for as long as possible should always be the objective.

Below advice on how to keep enjoying having meals with others for as long as possible:

Posture:
Sit upright during the meal. Remain seated after the meal for 15-20 minutes to allow the meal to 'go down'.

Swallow rate:
Don't rush the next bite of food. Eat slowly. Don't be in a hurry to add the next bite, but take time to leisurely chew the food and to swallow well. Place the fork provisionally to one side. Pick it up again once an extra ensuing swallow has been completed. Include pauses if the meal is drawn out. Take small bites at a time. The same applies to drinking; don't suddenly take a couple of sips in succession, but drink drop for drop and again complete an extra swallow. Take care that the quantities aren't too large. This applies to both eating and drinking: pay attention to your breathing; if you become breathless then it's time to take a break.

Swallowing posture:
Try to swallow with the head tilted forwards and the chin slightly bent towards the chest. This technique can be used with both eating and drinking. Swallowing can even be perceived as being easier. This posture often benefits the passage of fluid/food through the upper oesophageal sphincter. In this position the upper oesophageal sphincter can relax.

Awareness and concentration:
Try to concentrate on the food and drink and your posture. Don't speak with your mouth full! After the meal, fully engage in the conversation. Ensure that you can see everyone around the table without having to turn your head too much.

onsistencies:

at and drink food and fluids, which you know are satisfying and leasant to swallow. Don't eat anything that's too hard, brittle or picy. You're more than capable of determining for yourself when he sensible option is to switch to finely mashed foods or bread vithout crusts or porridge. If necessary, use a thickening agent to elp condense watery fluids. You don't have to prove anything to nyone. What is most important is that you can independently eat nd drink in a way that's agreeable and suitable to you.

uality food:

ou can consult a dietician to discuss whether or not you're taking n sufficient energy and calories. They will help with modifications o ensure optimal nutritional intake.

atigue:

Rest a little longer than usual before commencing on your andwiches or evening meal. Chewing requires a great deal of ffort and your muscles can weaken while having a sandwich or vening meal. In these types of situations you're more prone to hoking because something lodges in your throat. Incorporate auses. Catch your breath. Avoid eating the last bit of food too uickly by taking large bites, and don't drain the final drops of our drink from the cup or glass. This prevents you from having o tilt your head too far back and swallowing at an oblique angle. This head position can lead to choking, especially with regard to drinking.

Spread:

f you're susceptible to a sudden onset of fatigue due to exertion, hen it's probably better if you divide the meals into smaller ortions and spread them throughout the day. We hereby hope hat, in combination with extra awareness for posture, chewing and swallowing, you are sufficiently safe to be able to enjoy your ood/drink. Assess your energy throughout the day. If your MS plays up at certain times, it's advisable to be extra careful in these moments with food/drink. You can also decide to consciously not eat/drink at these moments. Even the summer heat can aggravate the symptoms of MS. Look for somewhere cool or shady in the summer when you're eating or drinking.

Choking:

f you repetitive choke while drinking, then it's advisable to use a thickening agent. It allows you to condense fluids to a syrup- or honey thickness. Also swallow sip for sip.

Eating utensils:

Try to use cutlery and glassware as normally as possible. Drink from a regular glass or cup, sipping small quantities only. Take care when attempting to drain the final drops of fluid. Or leave the little of it in your cup or glass. Avoid using a straw. Sucking,

namely, requires extra effort and the combination of sucking and holding the straw in the mouth and safely swallowing can cost too much energy. Use customised eating- and drinking utensils if the muscle strength in your hand/arm requires it.

Dental hygiene:

Healthy teeth and/or a good prosthesis is necessary to be able to chew well. Even mouth hygiene in relation to having a dry mouth requires attention. Don't hesitate to see your dentist about any problems concerning your teeth.

Health care professionals:

If you are unable to eat and drink safely and independently, you can ask for support. Clearly indicate your likes and dislikes while being aided in eating/drinking. Let your caregiver read the advice and apply if necessary. The caregiver can also help you to use strategies recommended by the SLP. Let your caregiver inquire into the procedures surrounding severe choking. Your caregiver should be trained in CPR.

In conclusion:

The course of dysphagia is unique to everyone, as is MS. It can depict irregularities spreading over a period of years. Over the years relapses can occur that severely damage the swallowing function. Special swallowing techniques taught by an SLP or a diagnostic evaluation of swallowing may be needed in order to better assist your recovery. Nowadays, many hospitals have a Swallowing Team comprising of speech pathologists, ENT-doctors and radiologists. These are teams that specialise in testing for, advising in and treating dysphagia.

Should you require more information about how you and health professionals deal with your swallowing habits, then a single consultation, in discussion with your general practitioner, is advisable with a Swallowing Team in your area.

We hope that the above information encourages you to enjoy tasty food/drink for as long as possible.

G.J. Overbeek, clinical speech pathologist

7. Cooking with your children

Multiple sclerosis is the most common neurological disease among young adults (people under forty). This (often unexpected) life-event tends to arise in the demanding periods punctuating your life – those of graduating, applying for a job, buying a house or having children.

Fortunately, MS doesn't influence fertility and the chance of your child developing the disease in later life is minimal, owed mostly to the fact that MS isn't a hereditary disease.

If MS proves to be a huge debilitation in your daily life, then it can also affect how you care for and interact with your children. Whatever limitations MS may bring, you can always give your children love and attention. Sharing moments with your child in which he or she is assured of your undivided attention is defined as quality time with your child! And where better to create such moments than in the kitchen. Preparation of food is a daily task and one that can be a special time for just you and your child. Let your child:

- wash their hands
- roll up their sleeves
- put on an apron
- tie or fasten long hair.

Servings are for four persons.

Whopper pizza

Preparation time: 10 minutes / oven: 12 minutes

Necessary items: rolling pin, small knives, spoon, baking tray, baking paper

2 tablespoons flour
270 g pizza dough (ready-made)
1 jar tomato sauce (200 ml)
1 red sweet pepper, cut into pieces
8 black olives
4 mushrooms
a couple of sprigs of parsley
4 tablespoons mature cheese, grated

1 Preheat the oven to 200 °C.

2 Line the baking tray with the baking paper.

3 Sprinkle flour onto the work surface. Divide the dough into four pieces and roll with the rolling pin into 4 flat rustic circles.

4 Spread the tomato sauce onto the dough with the rounded side of the spoon.

5 Top the pizzas with pieces of sweet pepper, olives, mushrooms, parsley and grated cheese.

6 Put the pizzas on the baking tray and place in the oven. Cook for roughly 12 minutes until done.

Chocolate fondue

Preparation time: 10 minutes

Necessary items: small knife, 3 small dishes, pan, hotplate
4 slices of cake
250 g strawberries
250 g pineapple in pieces
300 g pure, dark chocolate
100 ml cream

1 Dice the cake and arrange in the dishes. Wash the strawberries. Allow the strawberries and pineapple to drain on kitchen paper, then divide evenly in the 4 dishes.

2 Break the chocolate over the pan. Add the cream. Melt the chocolate on a low heat and stir continuously until the sauce is nice and smooth.

3 Place the hotplate on the table and switch it on. Transfer the pan with the chocolate sauce to the hotplate.

4 Spear a piece of cake or fruit onto the fork and dredge it through the chocolate sauce.

Strawberry on a stick

Preparation time: 10 minutes / interval: 4 hours

Necessary items: small knife, electric mixer, fork, ice lolly moulds

300 g strawberries
60 g fine white sugar
500 ml yoghurt
1 teaspoon lemon juice

1 Wash the strawberries and cut off the tops with the knife. Slice the strawberries into pieces.

2 Purée the strawberries with the electric mixer. Take the fork and mix the ingredients well. Fill the ice lolly moulds with the strawberry mixture.

3 Put the lollies in the freezer for 3-4 hours until frozen.

Meatballs

Preparation time: 40 minutes

Necessary items: bowl, small plate, small frying pan

2 slices of bread, remove crust

drop of milk

400 g lean minced beef

2 tablespoons sweet soy sauce

2 tablespoons coarse mustard

50 g breadcrumbs

salt and (freshly ground) pepper

2 tablespoons liquid margarine

1 Put the breadcrumbs in the bowl and pour enough milk into the bowl so that the bread is completely soft.

2 Add the minced beef, half of the sweet soy sauce, half of the mustard, the breadcrumbs and salt and pepper and knead the ingredients thoroughly together.

3 Moisten your hands and divide the minced meat into four equal portions. Create four meatballs and put them on the plate.

4 Melt the margarine in the small frying pan on a medium heat. Wait until the butter turns brown, then add the meatballs to the pan; once the meatballs have browned on the underside, turn them carefully over. Be extremely careful because the fat can spatter.

5 Add just enough water to the frying pan to submerge the meatballs a little more than halfway. Stir in the remainder of the sweet soy sauce and mustard.

6 Cover the pan with a lid and allow the meatballs to cook a further 30 minutes.

Serving suggestion: boiled potatoes and red cabbage with apples.

Baked fish parcels

Preparation time: 40 minutes / oven: 40 minutes

Necessary items: cutting board, kitchen knife, non-stick pan, ladle, fat free baking paper, baking tray

2 leeks
1/2 small carrot
5 sprigs of parsley
4 firm white fish fillets (haddock, cod or tilapia)
    each 150 g
salt and (freshly ground) pepper
1 tablespoon olive oil
125 ml chicken stock
1 tablespoon sweet soy sauce
2 tablespoon lemon juice

1 Preheat the oven to 200 ºC.

2 Cut the white portion of the leek into thin strips. Scrape the carrot and cut thinly into strips. Finely chop the parsley.

3 Season the fish with salt and pepper.

4 Coat the non-stick pan with oil and cook the leek and carrot for 3-4 minutes until the carrot is al dente.

5 Add the chicken stock and sweet soy sauce and bring to the boil until almost all the water has evaporated. Mix in half the parsley and half the lemon juice.

6 Cut four 30 x 30 sheets of fat free baking paper. Scoop the vegetable mix onto the middle of the paper and place a piece of fish on the top of each. Sprinkle with parsley and drizzle with a little lemon juice.

7 Pull the edges of the paper together and roll them, securely enclosing the filling. Don't fold too tightly. This allows room for the resulting steam during baking.

8 Transfer the parcels onto the baking tray and place in the middle of a hot oven for 15-18 minutes. Remove from the oven and open the parcels at the table.

Serving suggestion: with mashed potatoes and a chilled salad.

Mamskebab with warm tortillas

Preparation time: 40 minutes

**Necessary items: kitchen knife, cutting board,
    bowl, skewers, barbecue or grill pan**
**500 g tender lamb (cuts from the neck or
    tenderloin)**
3 tablespoons lemon juice
3 tablespoons olive oil
1 clove of garlic, crushed
2 ripe tomatoes
1/4 cucumber
8 small corn tortillas
handful of lettuce leaves
if so desired, sour cream or garlic sauce

1 Put wooden skewers in lukewarm water for half
an hour to prevent them from splintering during
cooking.

2 Dice the meat in bite-size pieces. Put in the bowl
and add the lemon juice, oil and garlic.

3 Slice the tomatoes and cut the cucumber into
strips.

4 Spear the lamb onto the skewers. Cook on the
barbecue or in the grill pan for approximately
2 minutes on each side until completely brown.
It's not a problem if the meat is still a little pink
on the inside.

5 Arrange the kebabs on the warm tortillas and
serve with tomatoes, cucumber and lettuce. Add
a dollop of sour cream or garlic sauce to the dish,
if so desired.

Chicken in puff pastry shell

Preparation time: 30 minutes

**Necessary items: cutting board, knife, 2 pans,
large soup-ladle, small bowl, ladle, scissors**
400-500 ml chicken stock (stock cube or jar)
350 g cooked chicken
40 g butter
3 tablespoons flour
1 egg yolk
2 teaspoons lemon juice
125 ml cream
salt and (freshly ground) pepper
4 puff pastry shells (box)
1 sprig of parsley

1 Preheat the oven to 180 °C.

2 Pour the chicken stock into a pan and heat until almost to the boil.

3 Cut the chicken into small pieces.

4 Carefully melt the butter in a pan. Add the flour and stir well until smooth. Turn up the heat and let the mixture gently simmer for 1 minute. Be sure not to let it burn. Scoop in the stock little by little and keep stirring.

5 Transfer a little of the white sauce to the bowl and stir in the egg yolk. Return and mix in with the white sauce, add the lemon juice, cream and chicken pieces and stir well. Add salt and pepper to taste.

6 Firstly, remove the little cap and put the puff pastry shells into the oven to get nice and hot. Let your mother help you with this!

7 Chop the parsley fine with the scissors.

8 Fill the puff pastry shells with the ragout (that is the name of the sauce and chicken mixture), sprinkle with parsley and replace the little cap.

Pigs in a blanket

Preparation time: 10 minutes / oven: 15 minutes

**Necessary items: baking tray, small bowl,
    pastry brush**
1 egg
3 sheets of puff pastry
12 cocktail sausages
ketchup or mild salsa

1 Preheat the oven to 200 °C.

2 Lightly beat the egg in the bowl.

3 Cut the puff pastry sheets twice, diagonally, creating 4 triangles.

4 Place a cocktail sausage at the bottom point of the triangle and roll it up to the top. It should resemble a croissant. Ensure the sausage doesn't stick out too much, because it'll darken too much in the oven.

5 Place the finger food onto the baking tray and, using the pastry brush, coat lightly with the egg. Place in a hot oven for 15 minutes until golden brown.

6 Pour some ketchup or salsa into a small dish. Serve with the snacks and dip away!

Pancakes

Preparation time: 20 minutes

**Necessary items: bowl, whisk, frying pan,
   soup-ladle, spatula, 2 flat plates**

175 g flour
2 eggs
450 ml low fat milk
1 teaspoon sunflower oil
salt
2 tablespoon liquid margarine
icing sugar and syrup

Tip Ready everything and lay out ingredients and utensils (sieve, knives, baking tray, condiments etc.) in order of use, so that you finish when you've gone through the row of items. Measure necessary quantities beforehand.

1 Whisk the flour, eggs, milk, oil and pinch of salt together in the bowl until smooth.

2 Pour a little margarine into the frying pan, keeping the heat low. Using the soup-ladle, scoop some of the batter into the pan.

3 Cook the batter until the bubbles on top start breaking and the pancake is nearly set, then carefully flip using the spatula and cook the other side. When done, set onto a plate.

4 Cook the rest of the pancakes in the same way until the batter is finished. Cover the pancakes with a plate to keep them warm.

Eat warm with sugar or syrup, or both.

Baked stuffed apples

Preparation time: 10 minutes / oven: 45 minutes

Necessary items: peeler, apple corer, small knife, small bowl, oven dish, four small dishes

4 firm apples
2 tablespoons sultanas
1 tablespoon dark brown caster sugar
$1/3$ teaspoon cinnamon
25 g butter, diced
4 cinnamon sticks
25 g butter
500 ml vanilla custard

1 Preheat the oven to 190 °C.

2 Peel the top of the apples, approximately 3 cm from the stalk.

3 Remove the core with the apple corer, and a slice off the bottom so the apples remain upright.

4 Mix the sultanas with the brown caster sugar, cinnamon and diced butter. Stuff the apples with this mixture and embed a cinnamon stick into each one.

5 Grease the oven dish with the butter. Arrange the apples in the dish and cook for approximately 45 minutes in the hot oven. Remove the cinnamon sticks from the apples, be very careful, the apples are hot.

6 Put the apples into the dishes and drizzle with vanilla custard.

8. Cooking with cranberries

Chances are, sooner or later, you will encounter problems concerning your bladder function. The most common symptoms that present themselves are overstimulation of the bladder, where an urge arises to frequently urinate or the dysfunction itself prevents the bladder from completely emptying. Bladder dysfunctions aren't always heralded by symptoms, which means you're not always aware of a possible problem. It could be that you're unaware of the fact that your bladder is not completely empty. Or even that you have a bladder infection. And yet it is of vital importance to detect these dysfunctions as early as possible. This is where the MS specialist nurse is of particular importance. By regularly screening all MS sufferers the complications associated with MS can be prevented, thereby improving the quality of life.

A major problem associated with not being able to completely empty the bladder is the risk of creating a breeding ground for bacteria, which can lead to bacterial infections. Often, the only indication of a bladder dysfunction is the recurrence of a chronic bladder infection. A urinary tract infection can worsen MS symptoms, increase fatigue.

Research has shown that cranberries are preventive against urinary tract infection and can reduce the risk of recurring bladder infection. The active compounds in cranberries, called tannins, eliminate E. coli bacteria (80% responsible for infections).

These tannins, called proanthocyanidins or PACs, prevent E. coli from adhering to the cells in the bladder walls and urinary tract thus preventing infection.

Servings in this chapter are for four persons.

Red cabbage salad with cranberry dressing

Preparation time: 10 minutes

1 large apple
50 g cured ham
500 g finely chopped red cabbage
4 tablespoons cranberry compote
1-2 tablespoons (raspberry) vinegar
2 tablespoons sunflower oil
2 tablespoons water
salt and (freshly ground) pepper
6 slices toasted whole-wheat bread
150 g spreadable soft cheese with walnuts
   (Rambol)

1 Peel the apples and cut into pieces. Cut the ham into thin strips. Mix the red cabbage together with the apple and ham.

2 Make the dressing: Mix the cranberry compote together with the vinegar and whisk in the oil. Dilute the dressing with water and add salt and pepper to taste.

3 Spread the soft cheese onto the toast just before serving and cut into triangles.

4 Serve the bread and cheese with the salad.

Cranberry-Pecan bread

Preparation time: 50 minutes / oven: 15 minutes

1 pack white bread mix
300 ml lukewarm water
25 g butter at room temperature
1 teaspoon allspice
2 tablespoons maple syrup
100 g pecans, coarsely chopped
150 g dried cranberries

1 Knead the white bread mix with water in a bowl together with the butter and allspice, forming a smooth dough. Leave the dough in the bowl, cover with aluminium foil and allow to rise for 15 minutes.

2 Preheat the oven to 200 °C.

3 Knead the maple syrup, pecans and cranberries into the risen dough. Divide the dough into 12 equal portions and roll into balls. Again, leave to rise under a tea towel for 30 minutes.

4 Bake the rolls for 15 minutes until golden brown.

5 Allow to cool on a cooling tray.

Cranberry compote

Preparation time: 15 minutes

450 g cranberries
150 ml freshly squeezed orange juice
200 g sugar

Tip   Read new recipes a couple of days beforehand to get used to them. Highlight (for instance with a marker pen) keywords (ingredients, following order, cooking time etc.) in the text; it provides a quick and easy overview, while you're cooking, of what is normally hidden amid long sentences.

1 Wash the berries in a colander and allow to drain.

2 Bring the berries together with the orange juice to the boil in a pan. Uncover and softly cook until the berries pop open (4-5 minutes).

3 Take the pan from the heat and stir in the sugar. Stir continuously until all the sugar has dissolved.

4 Spoon the compote into a dish and allow to cool.

Banana smoothie with cranberry juice

Preparation time: 5 minutes / freezing: 1 hour

2 ripe bananas
1 l low fat yoghurt
400 ml cranberry juice
1 tablespoon liquid honey

1 Cut the bananas in slices. Put in a freezer bag and freeze for roughly 1 hour.

2 Put the frozen banana slices into a mixing cup. Add the yoghurt, cranberry juice and honey and blend with an electric mixer or blender into a frothy drink.

3 Pour the smoothie into four glasses.

9. Super Menu

If you're suffering from fatigue, make sure you surround yourself with people who are full of vigour. People who tend to sap your energy and your strength should be kept at arm's length. Invite friends to dinner who inspire, enliven and stimulate you. Meals are also an excellent way of conveying your gratitude to family and loved ones for their constant help and support; how about a heart-warming meal on a wintry night? Nice meals and festive get-togethers brighten up the year.

Don't be afraid to experiment, to develop your own touch or give your creativity free rein in the kitchen. Only then will you truly be able to receive people and enjoy each other's company along with delicious food.

Hereby a menu for 8 persons, for whenever family or friends drop by.

Toast with sweet pepper, tomato and goat cheese curls

Preparation time: 25 minutes

8 medium size slices of cottage loaf or French
  bread
75 ml mild olive oil
75 g seasoned goat's cheese
2 tins anchovies, drained
6 sprigs of fresh oregano
(freshly ground) peppercorns

For the tomato topping:
2 medium size tomatoes
1 clove of garlic, finely chopped
1 tablespoon mild olive oil
1 tablespoon finely chopped basil

For the sweet pepper topping:
2 roasted sweet peppers (jar), drained
1 tablespoon mild olive oil
1 teaspoon lemon juice

1 Preheat the oven to 190 °C. Drizzle the bread with oil, put the slices on a baking tray and cook for 10 minutes until golden brown.

2 For the tomato topping:
Clean and quarter the tomatoes. Remove the juice and seeds and finely chop the flesh. Mix the tomatoes with the garlic, oil and basil.

3 For the sweet pepper topping:
Cut the sweet pepper into small pieces. Mix with the oil and lemon juice.

4 Grate the cheese into coarse curls. Layer one half of the bread with the tomato topping and garnish liberally with the cheese curls. Layer the other half of the bread with the sweet pepper topping and anchovies and garnish with oregano and pepper.

Roasted entrecote with fresh herbs

Preparation time: approximately 1 hour

Main course

2 kg entrecote, one piece
salt and (freshly ground) black pepper
2 tablespoons finely chopped fresh herbs
  (rosemary, thyme, parsley)
4 tablespoons liquid margarine

1 Preheat the oven to 125 °C.

2 Flavour the meat with salt, pepper and fresh herbs, rub in well.

3 Heat the margarine in a frying pan and cook the meat until completely brown. Remove the meat from the pan and transfer to an oven dish – fatty side up. Stick a meat thermometer into the thickest part of the meat and place the dish in the preheated oven.

4 Cook the entrecote until the core temperature reaches 60 °C. Remove the meat from the oven dish, wrap in aluminium foil and allow to stand for 10 minutes. Cut the meat in attractive slices and garnish with rosemary.

Serving suggestion: with piped mashed potato, green beans and red wine sauce (see recipe on pg. 85).

Red wine sauce

Preparation time: 10 minutes

To accompany the main course

30 g butter
2 shallots, finely chopped
25 g flour
250 ml beef stock
100 ml red wine
1/2 teaspoon sugar
salt and (freshly ground) pepper

1. Heat the butter in a saucepan and sauté the shallots.

2. Stir in the flour and add the beef stock. Stir continuously. Allow the ingredients to boil down for a couple of minutes.

3. Add the wine, then mix in the sugar, salt and pepper to taste.

Serving suggestion: with entrecote, boiled potatoes and French beans.

Tip When you're trying out a recipe for the first time, choose a quiet moment and make a small portion, not an entire meal. Recipes are usually created for several people. You can easily divide the quantities by three or four.

Choux pastry dripping with chocolate

Preparation time: 20 minutes

Dessert
1 box of choux pastry (frozen)

For the butter caramel:
75 g fine white sugar
1/2 tablespoon water
20 g butter

For the chocolate drizzle:
75 g pure chocolate
50 g icing sugar
50 g butter

1 Allow the choux pastry to thaw. Arrange a portion of the choux pastry onto an attractive plate, creating two layers.

2 For the butter caramel:
Put the sugar and water in a heavy-bottomed pan. Let the mixture cook until golden brown. Stir in the butter. Dip a spoon in the caramel and drizzle over the choux pastry.

3 For the chocolate drizzle:
Melt the chocolate au bain-marie or in the microwave. Stir in the icing sugar and the butter. Keep stirring until the mixture is nice and smooth. Dip a spoon in the chocolate and drizzle over the choux pastry.

10. Extra dietary fibres

Constipation is a common ailment. The major cause is lack of fluid as food passes through the intestines and limited bowel movements. Decreased physical exercise slows down bowel activity and in addition, certain medications can impede bowel habits. Pain, depression and stress can also suppress intestinal activity.

Some people drink little in an attempt to reduce existing bladder dysfunctions, but for supple bowel activity the intestines require sufficient fluids. At least 1.2 litres of fluid is recommended per day. In addition, the intake of dietary fibres can also improve the intestinal function by making it easier for your body to move foods and waste product. Roughage or dietary fibres are indigestible carbohydrates. Dietary fibres are found in vegetables, fruit, whole-wheat products and legumes. They promote a feeling of fullness and improve digestion. Dietary fibres have a type of 'sponge effect'. That is, they absorb water as they move through the digestive system, resulting in softer stool and easier bowel movement.

Servings for four persons in this chapter.

Couscous with lamb and chickpeas

Preparation time: 1 hour and 45 minutes

600 g lamb, leg of lamb or top round
2 tomatoes
1 large carrot
1 small oxheart cabbage
1 tin of chickpeas (400 gram)
4 tablespoons oil
1 onion, chopped
1 teaspoon ground ginger
3 saffron threads
salt and (freshly ground) pepper
300 g couscous

1 Cut the meat into relatively large pieces (approximately 50 gram).

2 Peel the tomatoes and cut the flesh into pieces. Scrape the carrot and cut lengthwise down the middle. Proceed to cut into thin, finger length strips. Remove the heart from the oxheart cabbage. Cut the cabbage lengthwise down the middle and cut each half again in 3-4 parts. Rinse the chickpeas in a colander and allow to drain.

3 Heat 2 tablespoons of oil in a frying pan and stir-fry the meat until completely brown. Add the onion, ground ginger, saffron and pepper and salt to taste; stir-fry for a further 1 minute. Add the pieces of tomato and enough warm water to barely submerge the meat. Bring these ingredients to the boil, cover the pan with its lid and allow the meat to gently simmer for 30 minutes.

4 Add the carrot and the cabbage and allow the meat to cook for approximately 30 minutes. Stir in the drained chickpeas for the remaining 5 minutes of cooking time.

5 In the meantime, soak the couscous according to the package directions. Stir with a fork to loosen the grains, add the rest of the oil and salt and pepper to taste. Transfer the couscous onto a flat dish and spoon the lamb on top.

Bulgur salad

Preparation time: 40 minutes

175 g bulgur
175 ml vegetable stock, lukewarm
juice of 2 lemons
1 tablespoon tomato purée
1/2 chilli pepper, seedless, finely chopped
4 spring onions, cut in rings
4 tablespoons finely chopped smooth parsley
3 tablespoons finely chopped mint
4 tablespoons pine nuts
3 tablespoons olive oil
ground paprika

1 Pour the lukewarm vegetable stock over the bulgur and allow to soak for 30 minutes. Drain the excess liquid away and loosen the grains with the tops of the fingers.

2 Mix the bulgur together with the lemon juice, tomato purée, chilli pepper, spring onion, parsley, mint and pine nuts. Spoon the mixture into a dish and sprinkle lightly with ground paprika.

Whole-wheat granary loaf

Preparation time: 15 minutes / rising and oven: 1 hour

500 g whole wheat bread mix
oil
25 g pine nuts
40 g pumpkin seeds
40 g sunflower seeds
25 g wheat flakes

1 Mix the bread mix with 300 ml of lukewarm water and a tablespoon of oil. Knead the mixture for roughly 10 minutes to form a smooth dough. Add 15 grams of pine nuts, 15 grams of pumpkin seeds and 15 grams of sunflower seeds. Knead the dough once more, evenly distributing the seeds throughout. Place the dough in a bowl, cover with cling film and allow to rise for 30 minutes in a warm place.

2 Preheat the oven to 225 °C.

3 Mix the remaining seeds and wheat flakes together in a deep dish. Knead the dough again thoroughly, divide into two equal portions and roll into balls. Coat the top of the dough with a little water and press in the seed mixture. Press the seeds firmly in place. Place the bread rolls onto a baking tray, allowing enough room for them to rise during baking.

4 Place the bread rolls in the preheated oven. Atomise the inside of the oven with a plant/water spray. Bake the bread for 20-25 minutes until brown. Allow the bread to thoroughly cool for 5 minutes on a cooling tray.

5 Bread making machine: fill the mould with water and add the whole-wheat bread mix with 1 tablespoon of oil. Mix all the seeds and wheat flakes into the dough at the moment the machine requires it. Bake the bread in the machine.

Caribbean bean stew

Preparation time: 40 minutes

3 tablespoons olive oil
1 large onion, coarsely chopped
3 cloves of garlic, coarsely chopped
1/2 chilli pepper, seedless, finely chopped
1 small tin tomato purée (70 g)
2 teaspoons ground cumin
1 teaspoon oregano
4 ripe tomatoes, cut into pieces
500 g pumpkin, diced
1 tin butter beans (400 g)
1 tin kidney beans (400 g)

1 tin of corn (300 g)
salt and (freshly ground) pepper

1 Heat the oil in a wok or frying pan and gently sauté the onion, garlic and pepper until their aromas release. Stir in the tomato purée, cumin and oregano and cook for a further 2 minutes. Add the tomatoes and stew the ingredients to make a creamy sauce.

2 Stir the pumpkin into the sauce and cook on a medium heat for 20 minutes.

3 Drain the beans and corn, then add to the pumpkin mixture. Heat the mixture for a further 5 minutes. Add salt and pepper to taste.

Serving suggestion: with rice or bread and crudités.

Potato salad with artichoke and cashew nuts

Preparation time: 20 minutes

800 g waxy potatoes, peeled
150 g green beans, halved
salt and (freshly ground) pepper
1 tin artichoke hearts, drained
150 g unsalted cashew nuts
1 1/2 tablespoons wine vinegar
1 teaspoon mustard
4-5 tablespoons olive oil
2 teaspoons fresh thyme leaves
75 g lamb's lettuce
100 g young leaf lettuce

1 Dice the potatoes 2 centimetres in size. Cook the potatoes and green beans in salt water for 6-8 minutes until al dente. Rinse in a colander with cold water.

2 Quarter the artichoke hearts. Roast the cashew nuts in a dry pan until golden brown.

3 Take a large bowl and whisk the vinegar, mustard, olive oil and thyme to make the dressing. Add salt and pepper to taste. Add the potatoes, beans and artichoke hearts, then loosely blend in the lamb's lettuce, young leaf lettuce and half the nuts. Sprinkle the remaining nuts over the salad.

11. Cooking al fresco

Being outdoors is very healthy. The effect of nature on humans is beneficial. Being amongst nature promotes more energy, less stress and better health. Spend more time out of doors: on the moors, in the woods, taking a walk along the fields or a wonderful trip to the beach. In addition to walking- and cycle routes, there are currently other routes available to, and suitable for, electric bikes, mopeds or mobility scooters.

The summer is an ideal time for eating al fresco and the garden lends itself as an excellent cooking space. This chapter includes recipes for summer buffets, picnic outings, beach parties and barbecues. The recipes are straightforward and make use of ingredients that are simple to use and easy to find.

Set the table, hang lanterns in the garden and drape something to ward off the sun, and enjoy the dishes that look great and taste amazing.

Beach party

The beach can be a fantastic location for a lively meal. It needn't be terribly difficult. A couple of disposable barbecues, upside down crates to sit on, a couple of inviting dishes for the grill, some bread, dip sauces and salads. Et voila! The barbecue dishes can be prepared at home beforehand and taken to the beach wrapped in aluminium foil.

Servings are for four persons.

Chicken spare rib parcel with Italian vegetables

Preparation time: 35 minutes

2 red onions, peeled and cut thinly in rings
2 red sweet peppers, remove seeds and thinly
   cut into strips
2 small courgette, cut in 0,5 cm slices
125 g chestnut mushrooms, sliced
1 tablespoon dried oregano
2 tablespoons balsamic vinegar
4 tablespoons traditional olive oil
salt and (freshly ground) pepper
1 kg marinated honey chicken spare ribs
   (approximately 12 pieces)
aluminium foil to make the parcels

1 Evenly divide the onion, sweet pepper, courgette
and mushrooms over the pieces of aluminium
foil. Sprinkle with oregano and drizzle with
the balsamic vinegar and 3 tablespoons of oil.
Sprinkle with salt and pepper to taste. Place the
chicken spare ribs on top of the vegetables and
fold the aluminium foil.

2 Place the parcels for roughly 10 minutes on the
barbecue. Turn after 5 minutes. Remove the
chicken spare ribs from the parcel and coat
with the remainder of the oil. Return to the hot
barbecue for approximately 15 minutes and cook
until completely brown.

Cajun shrimp with bacon

Preparation time: 20 minutes

12 large, uncooked, unpeeled shrimp (frozen)
12 slices of bacon
2 teaspoons Cajun seasoning or seasoning for
   doner kebab
2 tablespoons sunflower oil
12 skewers

Tip   Make as much as possible beforehand. You can then prepare other more elaborate dishes and put them in the fridge or freezer until ready for use.

1 Place wooden skewers in water for 15 minutes.

2 Allow the shrimp to thaw. Peel and remove the dark digestive tract. Wash the shrimp in cold water and pat dry with kitchen paper.

3 Spear each shrimp lengthwise onto the skewer and wrap in a slice of bacon.

4 Stir the Cajun seasoning into the oil and coat the shrimp with this mixture.

5 Place the shrimp on the barbecue for approximately 2 minutes on each side until nice and golden brown.

Serving suggestion: with aioli mayonnaise.

Stuffed sweet mini peppers

Preparation time: 20 minutes

8 orange sweet mini peppers
1 tablespoon olive oil
150 g minced beef
75 g feta cheese
1 tablespoon Mexican seasoning
1 tablespoon coriander, finely chopped
8 slices of bacon

1 Slice the sweet mini peppers open lengthwise on one side and remove the seeds. Cook in a pan of boiling water for 2-3 minutes until al dente. Drain in a colander.

2 Heat the oil in a pan. Cook the minced beef, stirring it loose.

3 Crumble the feta cheese and add it, together with the Mexican seasoning and coriander, to the minced beef. Stuff the sweet pepper with this minced beef filling and squeeze tightly closed. Wrap with a slice of bacon.

4 Secure the sweet mini peppers between a barbecue clamp or wrap them in aluminium foil. Place on the grill and allow to cook on a medium warm barbecue for approximately 10 minutes until golden brown. Serve warm with salad, bread and dip sauce.

Rocket (rucola) and red grapefruit salad

Preparation time: 10 minutes

1 red grapefruit
100 g mixed young leaf lettuce
30 g rocket (rucola)
10 green olives
2 tablespoons lemon juice
3 tablespoons olive oil
salt and (freshly ground) pepper

1 Peel the grapefruit, remove the pith and membrane and cut the segments in half. Wash the lettuce and rocket.

2 Mix together the lettuce, rocket, grapefruit and olives.

3 Whisk the lemon juice and the oil together to make the dressing. Add salt and pepper to taste. Toss the salad with the dressing.

Aioli

Preparation time: 40 minutes

2 whole, fresh garlic bulbs
2 tablespoons mayonnaise
1 tablespoon lemon juice
Tabasco sauce

1 Preheat the oven to 200 °C.

2 Place the garlic bulbs for 30 minutes in the middle of the oven. Remove from the oven and cut the peak off of the bottom. Use a knife to remove the roasted garlic pulp (the rest is unusable).

3 Finely chop the garlic pulp and mix together with the mayonnaise. Stir in the lemon juice and season the mayonnaise with a few drops of Tabasco sauce.

Muffins with rhubarb filling

Preparation time: 35 minutes / interval: 1 hour

250 g flour
1/2 sachet of dry yeast (7 g)
1 teaspoon salt
1 tablespoon sugar
1 teaspoon cinnamon
1/2 teaspoon ground cumin
1/2 teaspoon ground ginger
200 ml lukewarm milk
1 tablespoon oil
250 g rhubarb compote

1 Mix the flour, yeast, salt, sugar, cinnamon, ground cumin and ground ginger together in a bowl. Add the milk and blend the ingredients together. Cover the bowl with a towel and allow the dough to rise for 1 hour in a warm place.

2 Preheat the oven to 180 °C.

3 Grease a muffin pan with butter or use 8 well-greased paper cupcake forms. Spoon two tablespoons of dough into each form and bake the muffins in the middle of the oven for 20 minutes until golden brown.

4 Remove the muffins from the oven and allow to cool. Cut the muffins open and fill with the rhubarb compote.

Grilled tuna fish in sesame marinade

Preparation time: 5 minutes / interval: 1 hour

For the marinade:
3 tablespoons olive oil
1 tablespoon sesame oil
1 tablespoon lemon juice
1 cm fresh ginger root, finely grated
2 tablespoons sesame seeds
2 tablespoons fresh coriander, finely chopped
salt and (freshly ground) pepper

4 fresh tuna fillets 2 cm thick

1 Mix the ingredients for the marinade together.

2 Rinse the tuna with cold water and pat dry with kitchen paper. Place the tuna fillets in a dish and pour on the marinade. Cover and allow the fish to marinade for 1 hour* in the fridge. Turn the fish after half an hour.

3 Place the tuna on a very hot! barbecue. Cook each side for 2 minutes. The fillets shouldn't be wholly cooked-through.

* Marinade the tuna no longer than 4 hours.

Tip   If you enjoy being outdoors and the lifestyle it affords, then cooking al fresco is a revolution and extremely popular as well.

Lentil burgers with pineapple salsa

Preparation time: 25 minutes

100 pineapple in pieces, finely chopped
1 spring onion, cut into rings
2 teaspoons sambal ulek
1 tablespoon lemon juice
2 tablespoons fresh coriander, finely chopped
6 slices old whole-wheat bread
100 ml full-fat milk
3 tablespoons oil
1 onion, chopped
1/2 tablespoon curry powder
1 tin of lentils (400 g) drained

1-2 tablespoons soy sauce
salt and (freshly ground) pepper
2-3 tablespoons breadcrumbs
oil to coat

1 First make the salsa: Put the pineapple, spring onion, sambal, lemon juice and coriander in a bowl. Mix and allow to stand for 15 minutes.

2 Soak the bread in the milk.

3 Heat 1 tablespoon of oil in a saucepan and sauté the onion with the curry powder for 2-3 minutes.

4 Drain the bread well and mix in the blender together with the lentils, onion mixture and soy sauce until the ingredients form a thick purée. Add salt and pepper to taste, and if necessary breadcrumbs should the purée not be thick enough. Create four burgers.

5 Fold a piece of aluminium foil double and coat with oil. Place the burgers on the oil-coated foil. Place on a hot barbecue and cook both sides for roughly 6 minutes until brown.

Serve the lentil burgers with the pineapple salsa.

Semi-matured cheese and strawberry salad

Preparation time: 15 minutes

200 g sugar snap peas
salt and (freshly ground) pepper
250 g strawberries
200 g semi-matured cheese
4 tablespoons strawberry jam
2 tablespoons red wine vinegar
6 tablespoons olive oil
1 tablespoon mint, finely chopped
150 g lamb's lettuce
2 tablespoons sunflower seeds

1 Cook the sugar snap peas in salt water for 2 minutes until al dente. Rinse in cold water in a colander and allow to drain.

2 Wash the strawberries, remove the tops and cut lengthwise in half. Dice the cheese.

3 Heat the strawberry jam in a pan with a tablespoon of water until the jam liquefies. Pour the jam into a bowl and whisk in the vinegar, oil and chopped mint. Toss half the dressing with the lamb's lettuce.

4 Arrange the lamb's lettuce, sugar snap peas, strawberries, cheese and sunflower seeds onto the plates. Garnish with the remainder of the dressing.

Potato salad with dill

Preparation: 45 minutes / interval: 1 hour

1 kg waxing potatoes
200 ml warm vegetable stock
2 tablespoons finely chopped dill + extra to
    garnish
200 ml sour cream
salt and (freshly ground) pepper
2 red onions, chopped
1 bunch of radishes, sliced

1 Scrub the potatoes clean and cook with the skin for approximately 20 minutes. Peel the potatoes while still as warm as possible, slice and pour on the warm vegetable stock. Allow the potatoes to stand for 30 minutes.

2 Mix the dill with the sour cream. Add salt and pepper to taste. Blend the onion, radish and sauce with the potatoes.

3 Leave the potatoes for 1 hour in the fridge to enhance the taste.

4 Arrange the salad onto the plates and garnish with dill.

Agua fresca with melon

Preparation time: 10 minutes

1 lime
1 small ripe honeydew melon
4 tablespoons sugar
750 ml ice-cold water
sprigs of fresh mint

1 Squeeze the limes.

2 Peel the melon, cut in half and remove the seeds. Cut 4 thin segments of the fruit and keep to one side. Cut the rest of the melon into small pieces and purée in a blender together with the sugar, water and lime juice. Pour the mixture into tall glasses or into a pitcher.

3 Garnish the agua fresca with the melon segments and mint.

Serving suggestion: with crushed ice cubes.

Indian naan bread with chicken curry and pumpkin

Preparation time: 20 minutes

2 natural half-baked Indian naan breads
200 g pumpkin
300 g chicken fillet
2 tablespoons oil
1 tablespoon curry powder
salt and (freshly ground) pepper
100 ml coconut milk
1 tablespoon lemon juice
1 cup alfalfa sprouts

Tip What is better than a walk in the forest or a trip to the park? Fun with the family, friends or kids going on a jaunt. Cosy with just the two of you, idling lazily on the grass or reading a book. Of course, a packed picnic basket or cool box shouldn't be forgotten.

1. Bake the naan bread according to the package directions.

2. Peel and dice the pumpkin. Cut the chicken fillet into strips.

3. Heat the oil in a pan and stir-fry the chicken pieces together with the pumpkin and curry powder for 2 minutes on a high heat. Add salt and pepper to taste. Stir in the coconut milk and lemon juice and allow the ingredients to simmer for a further 4 minutes.

4. Cut the naan bread crosswise through the middle and layer with the alfalfa and chicken curry. Wrap in aluminium foil and put in the fridge until time to leave.

Multi-grain Waldkorn bread with two cheeses

Preparation time: 10 minutes

4 slices of Waldkorn bread
40 g cream cheese
salt and (freshly ground) pepper
6 radishes, finely chopped
1 tub rucola cress or garden cress
4 slices mustard cheese

1 Cut the radishes into thin strips.

2 Spread the slices of Waldkorn bread with the cream cheese and sprinkle with salt and pepper to taste. Arrange the radishes on top. Cut the mustard cheese into strips and layer on top of the sandwich. Garnish with the rucola or garden cress.

3 Wrap the sandwiches in cling film and place in a lunch box. Put in the fridge until time to leave.

Rolled pancakes with strawberry cream

Preparation time: 10 minutes

50 ml cream
100 g cream cheese
3 tablespoons strawberry jam
4 ready-made plain pancakes

1 Whisk the cream until stiff. Whisk the cream cheese together with the strawberry jam and stir in the whipped cream.

2 Coat the pancakes partially with the strawberry cream, then roll up.

3 Cut the pancakes in half and wrap in cling film. Put in the fridge until time to leave.

Orange-strawberry smoothie

Preparation time: 10 minutes

250 g strawberries, washed
250 ml fresh orange juice
600 ml low-fat yoghurt, chilled
1 tablespoon honey
4 small sprigs of fresh mint

1 Keep 4 attractive strawberries to one side to garnish and put the rest in the blender or food processor.

2 Add the orange juice, yoghurt and honey and blend to a frothy drink.

3 Pour the smoothie into tall glasses and garnish with the strawberry and a sprig of mint.

Tip Finding it difficult to do good on the daily recommended quantity of fruit? Consider having a smoothie! Smoothies are delicious, refreshing and healthy (chilled) drinks made from fresh or frozen fruit.

Buttermilk smoothie

Preparation time: 15 minutes

100 g carrots, sliced
salt and (freshly ground) pepper
1 teaspoon sugar
2 ripe peaches or 4 halves from a tin
1 lime
500 ml buttermilk

1 Cook the carrots with the salt and sugar for 5 minutes. Purée the carrots and allow to cool.

2 Peel the peaches, if necessary, and purée the pulp.

3 Scrub the lime clean under running water and thinly grate 1 teaspoon of the zest. Cut the lime in half and squeeze the juice.

4 Mix together the carrot- and peach purée with the lime zest, 1 tablespoon of lime juice and the buttermilk. Add salt and pepper to the drink to taste.

5 Pour the smoothie into tall glasses.

Lemon smoothie

Preparation time: 10 minutes

125 g strawberries
200 g low-fat lemon quark
2 tablespoons Karvan Cevitam (concentrated
   fruit syrup) lemon
10 ice cubes

1 Wash the strawberries with cold water and remove the top.

2 Purée the strawberries in a blender or electric mixer. Add the quark, concentrated lemon syrup and ice cubes. Mix to form a smooth mixture. Add cold water if necessary.

3 Pour the smoothie into tall glasses.

Rooibos shake with melon

Preparation time: 10 minutes / interval: 1 hour

1 sachet rooibos tea
500 ml water
1 cinnamon stick
1 sachet vanilla sugar
250 g melon, peeled

1. Boil the water and make the rooibos tea in a teapot. Add the cinnamon stick and stir in the vanilla sugar.

2. After 10 minutes remove the cinnamon stick and the tea bag. Allow the tea to cool for 1 hour in the fridge until chilled.

3. Cut 4 thin pieces of the melon. Purée the rest of the melon with an electric mixer. Keep whisking and add the cold tea.

4. Pour the shake into tall glasses and garnish with a piece of melon.

Tomato-pesto shake

Preparation time: 5 minutes

6 tomatoes
6 thin stalks of celery
600 ml plain yoghurt
1 tablespoon red pesto
salt and (freshly ground) pepper

1 Peel the tomatoes and cut into pieces.

2 Wash the celery stalks, remove any loose strands from the sides. Cut two stalks into small pieces.

3 Purée the tomatoes, pieces of celery and yoghurt with an electric mixer or blender. Add the pesto, salt and pepper to taste.

4 Pour the shake into four tall glasses and garnish with a stalk of celery.

Avocado-lime shake with coriander

Preparation time: 10 minutes

2 limes
2 ripe avocados
400 ml plain yoghurt
2 tablespoons finely chopped coriander
300 ml sparkling mineral water
10 drops of Tabasco
salt and (freshly ground) pepper

1 Squeeze one of the limes, the other is to garnish.

2 Cut the avocados in half and remove the seed. Spoon the pulp out and drizzle with lime juice.

3 Purée the avocado, yoghurt and coriander with an electric mixer or blender until smooth. Add the mineral water while mixing to produce a frothy drink.

4 Add Tabasco, salt and pepper to the shake to taste.

5 Pour the shake into 4 tall glasses and garnish with pieces of lime.

12. Cooking with love

This cookbook ends on a note of love. A pleasant and positive conclusion in which life is celebrated. That is good for your family life or social contacts and your work. This way you keep your relationships solid and elevate your quality of life.

When MS is diagnosed, it has an inevitable effect on your partner. Interest in each other can wane because of the intense changes you can both go through as a result of a chronic disease – symptoms, limitations and stress. It is important to keep your love and your relationship alive. Plan a moment where you both can be alone with each other and choose a dish that you would both truly like to make. This can be a family recipe, but you can also choose something completely original. Prepare the meal together. Share the kitchen and the tasks, and cook together. Play music that elicits good memories for you both. These are all ingredients to ensure you make time for each other.

Servings in this chapter are for the two lovers cooking. Chose from the recipes and create your own menu.

Spicy cheese fondue

Preparation time: 15 minutes

400 ml dry white wine
100 g cream cheese
150 g blue cheese (Roquefort, Gorgonzola,
    Danish Blue)
350 g grated semi-matured cheese
1 tablespoon corn flour
3 tablespoons gin
freshly ground white pepper
French bread
toasted cornbread
chicory leaves
pear, in pieces

1 Heat the wine in the fondue pan until it starts to boil. Turn down the heat. Add all the cheese and stir until the cheese melts. The mixture shouldn't boil.

2 Mix the corn flour and the gin to a smooth paste and add to the melted cheese, stirring continuously. Add pepper to the fondue to taste.

3 Serve the fondue with the bread, chicory and pear.

Love soup

Preparation time: 5 minutes

1 kg tomatoes
2 onions
2 cloves of garlic
500 ml vegetable stock
1 teaspoon dried thyme
salt and (freshly ground) pepper
125 ml crème fraîche
a couple of sprigs of parsley

1 Wash the tomatoes and cut in half. Peel the onions and the garlic. Finely chop the onions and the garlic.

2 Bring the vegetable stock, tomatoes, onions, garlic and thyme to the boil in a large pan. Cook for approximately 20 minutes.

3 Purée the tomato soup with an electric mixer. Add salt and pepper to taste.

4 Ladle the tomato soup into bowls. Add a dollop of crème fraîche and a sprinkle of parsley to each bowl.

Tip Serving suggestion: with crispy cheese butterflies. Buy them ready-made or bake them yourself. Create butterfly forms from puff pastry. Brush with lightly beaten egg. Sprinkle with Parmesan cheese. Place on a baking tray and cook for 20 minutes in a preheated oven at 200 °C.

Mushroom soufflé with truffle oil

Preparation time: 20 minutes / oven: 20 minutes

50 g dried porcini (penny bun)
butter for greasing
1 tablespoon sunflower oil
50 g mushrooms, chopped
salt and (freshly ground) pepper
10 g butter
10 g flour
12,5 ml water from the porcini
1 egg
1 teaspoons truffle oil

1 Wash the porcini with hot water. Allow to soak for 15 minutes in 2 dl of hot water. Preheat the oven (without convection) to 175 °C. Grease two soufflé dishes or heat resistant ramekins.

2 Remove the mushrooms from the water and finely chop. Strain the water used for soaking and retain it. Heat the oil in a pan. Cook the porcini and mushrooms for 2 minutes on a high heat. Add salt and pepper to taste. Allow to cool.

3 Melt the butter in a pan and stir in the flour. Cook for 1 minute on a low heat, stirring continuously. Add the filtered water a little at a time and keep stirring, producing a smooth sauce. Take the pan from the heat.

4 Separate an egg. Whisk the egg white until it stiffens. Mix the yolk in with the slightly cooled sauce. Blend in the egg white.

5 Divide the sauce between the two soufflé dishes. Cook for 20 minutes until golden brown.

6 Remove the soufflés from the oven and drizzle with the truffle oil. Serve.

Beef tournedos with mustard sauce...or.....................................

Preparation time: 15 minutes

2 pieces of beef tenderloin, 150 g (not flattened)
2 slices of bacon
25 g butter
2 tablespoons Armagnac or cognac
1 tablespoon sharp Dijon mustard
125 ml cream
salt and (freshly ground) pepper
2 sprigs of thyme

1 Wrap each piece of meat with a slice of bacon.

2 Heat the butter in a pan until the froth dissipates. Cook the meat for 4-6 minutes. Nice and brown on the outside, but pink on the inside. Turn the meat over half way through.

3 Drizzle some Armagnac onto the meat and allow the liquid to evaporate.

4 Place the meat onto a heated plate and cover with aluminium foil. Stir the mustard and cream into the leftover fat in the pan and stir the residue at the bottom free. Allow the liquid to boil down on a high heat until a smooth sauce remains.

5 Add salt and pepper to the sauce to taste, and mustard if desired. Place the tournedos onto two warm plates and spoon the sauce on top. Garnish with sprigs of thyme.

Serving suggestion: with grilled half tomatoes and green bean salad with spring onion and chopped black olives.

.... Baked red mullet with spicy sweet pepper sauce

Preparation time: 20 minutes

100 g fresh tagliatelle
4 tablespoons olive oil
1 small onion, chopped
1 yellow sweet pepper, coarsely chopped
150 ml vegetable stock
 juice of 1 orange
1 tablespoon sweet chilli sauce
salt and (freshly ground) pepper
2 red mullets in the skin

1 Cook the tagliatelle according to the package directions.

2 Heat 1 tablespoon of olive oil in a pan and sauté the onion and sweet pepper. Cover the pan with its lid and allow the ingredients to simmer for 5 minutes on a low heat.

3 Add the vegetable stock and orange juice and allow the sauce to cook for 10 minutes over medium heat. Purée the sauce with an electric mixer. Add the chilli sauce and salt and pepper to taste. If desired, dilute the sauce with a little water.

4 Sprinkle the fish with salt and pepper.

5 Heat the remainder of the oil in a pan. Bake the fish in the skin for 3 minutes over high heat. Turn the fish over and cook this side for 1 minute.

6 Arrange the fish on a bed of tagliatelle with the spicy sweet pepper sauce. Serve with a green salad.

Fig cakes

Preparation time: 20 minutes

**6 thin slices of Indonesian layered cake
  (spekkoek)**
fig jam
1 fresh fig

1 Spread fig jam on one side of the slices of layered cake and form two stacks of cake. Cut out two round forms from each of the stacks.

2 Quarter the fig and place a segment on each round stack.

Bitter almond cookies with pistachio filling

Preparation time: 20 minutes

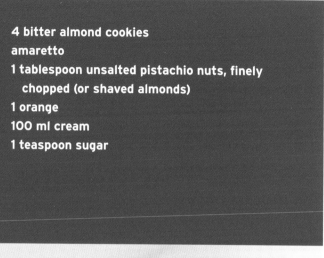

4 bitter almond cookies
amaretto
1 tablespoon unsalted pistachio nuts, finely
   chopped (or shaved almonds)
1 orange
100 ml cream
1 teaspoon sugar

1 Hollow out the flattened side of the bitter almond cookies with a teaspoon and drizzle with a little amaretto.

2 Scrub the orange clean. Remove thin layers of the rind and finely chop.

3 Whisk the cream together with the sugar until stiff. Stir in the pistachio nuts and a pinch of orange rind.

4 Spoon a teaspoon of the filling into the scooped out cookies. Garnish with a piece of orange rind.

Strawberries and nougat with chocolate

Preparation time: 20 minutes

100 g strawberries
100 g pure chocolate
1 tablespoon cream
100 g nougat

1 Wash the strawberries, and keep the tops. Dry well.

2 Melt the chocolate au bain-marie and stir in the tablespoon of cream.

3 Dip the strawberry and nougat half way into the chocolate and allow for the chocolate to harden.

Crème brûlée

Preparation time: 25 minutes

1 vanilla stick
200 ml cream
100 ml milk
60 g fine sugar
3 egg yolks
1 egg white
2 tablespoons of cane sugar

1 Preheat the oven to 140 °C. Cut the vanilla stick open. Bring the cream, milk, half of the fine sugar and the vanilla stick to the boil in a heavy-bottomed pan. Remove the pan from the heat and stir until the sugar is completely dissolved.

2 Blend the rest of the fine sugar with the yolk and egg white in a bowl. Add a couple of spoonsful of the cream mixture to the mix, then pour into the pan. Keep stirring.

3 Fill two oven dishes with the cream mixture. Place them in a roasting pan. Fill the pan with water to about 1/3 under the rim of the oven dishes. Put the roasting pan in the middle of the oven for 1 hour or until the crème brûlée feels firm (except the centre). Remove the dishes from the oven and allow to cool.

4 Preheat the grill.

5 Sprinkle the cane sugar on top of the crème brûlée. Place the dishes under the grill until the sugar melts or, using a burner, burn a layer of caramel on top of the crème.

Appendix: Ergonomics

Electrical appliances can save you a lot of time and energy, especially during the preparation of food. Machines can be largely relied upon for chopping and cutting, certainly in cases of loss of feeling in the hands. Additionally, kitchenware and cutlery fitted with sturdy and customised grips are pleasant and invaluable aids for those with sensory disturbances. Hand and finger guards are also useful when preparing food. But other symptoms, such as fatigue, muscle weakness and lack of coordination often influence your cooking habits too. Fortunately, nowadays there are many and varied types of culinary items available that can help you carry out your tasks in the kitchen.

A (mobile) kitchen stool can, for example, be of use in cases of reduced mobility or fatigue. But what if there is weakening of the muscle in one arm or hand? Then, there are countless ergonomic utensils available to help reduce the strain on your arm or hand. And special tin-, pan- or bottle openers are also available for those who only have one good functioning arm and hand.

In addition, the use of an anti-slip mat on the work surface in the kitchen is a very practical idea. It prevents your cutting board or mixing bowl from flying onto the floor.

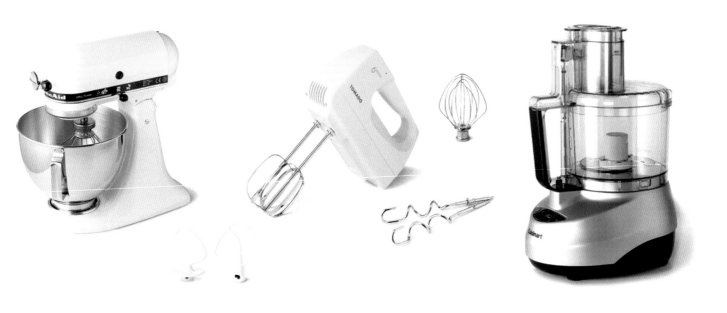

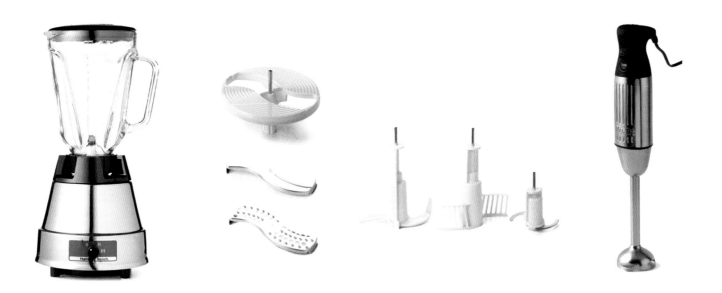

Thank you!

'Is there actually a cookbook for people with Multiple Sclerosis?'
What began as a question from one person evolved into a project on which a large group of people have been enthusiastically working for an entire year. Many people have helped me realise what merely began as a question.

Firstly, I would like to thank Frits Poiesz from Poiesz Publishing. I was fortunate enough to come into contact with Poiesz; a publishing house with years of experience in publishing cookbooks. Frits, you optimised the preconditions and guided me every step of the way through the various stages of this book's development. I have fond memories of our conversations while sitting around the table in my home. Thank you for the fine partnership.

Gijs Overbeek, speech-language pathologist and part of the swallowing team at the Medical Spectrum Twente, thank you for your input on the subject of dysphagia associated with MS. You have a great deal of experience with regard to neurological patients and I'm so grateful that you immediately liked the idea behind this book and was prepared to extend your cooperation.

MS-neurologist Dr. Jik Nihom, whose professional knowledge contributed to the medical integrity of this book. Jik, I'm fortunate to be able to work with you every day and greatly appreciated your input and in-depth review of the manuscript.

Culinary editor Corry Dusquesnoy, thank you for your expert advice and improvements. You have truly enhanced this book on every level.

My sister Kirsten, who supported me and helped with the manuscript. Thank you for the touching foreword.
Due to her background in dietetics, she was able to cast a very critical eye over the manuscript and suggested important additions. Petra van de Vis, thank you!

Niels and Laura van Gemert, it is a joy to have such a sweet son and daughter. Your help with the chapter 'Cooking with children' was invaluable to mama. You selected the recipes yourselves, which led to some surprising choices. Thank you sweethearts, because who knows better now what children like to cook than the children themselves?

Dear Wim, thank you very much for your input, ideas and support. Thanks to you this book achieved the necessary 'flow'.

Many thanks to Therese Burk and Dr. Anita Rose whose invaluable review and additions contributed to the realisation of this English edition. Cheers!

Last but not least, huge thanks to Cecilia, Barend, Henriëtte, Joyce, Anna, Christina, Monique, Huub, Jan, Tanja, Colette, Anneke, Martijn and all my family and friends who have supported me.

Astrid

Index